FINDING THE MONEY

FINDING *the* MONEY

A Guide to Paying Your Medical Bills

DIANE PAMMENTER TOLLEY

FINDING THE MONEY

published by Diane Pammenter Tolley

© 2001 by Diane Pammenter Tolley

Cover design by His Image Design Works

The Living Bible (TLB) © by Tyndale House Publishers

Printed in the United States of America

For information:

Diane Tollley•P.O. Box 971•Bend, Oregon 97709

01 02 03 04 05—10 9 8 7 6 5 4 3 2 1 0

TABLE OF CONTENTS

There are three things that remain—
faith, hope, and love—
and the greatest of these is
Love.
1 CORINTHIANS 13:13, TLB

This book is dedicated to those three ideals. How well I have learned them over the last eleven years, the years since my daughter Shelly was diagnosed with non-Hodgkin's lymphoma.

I dedicate this to those who continue to maintain the faith that they can still do something, despite the tall obstacles—those people who won't take no for an answer.

I dedicate this to those with the faith that they can survive, grow, and be better for all that they continue to go through. I dedicate this also to those who reach out and offer hope through helping hands and hearts, those willing to try to solve the problems that seem unsolvable…problems we know *can* be overcome.

Most of all, I dedicate this book to all the incredible people who have walked this walk, who have come into my life to teach me more about life and love than I thought the world held; to those who continue to show intense love for life even when they know their lives here on earth are about to end and; lastly, to those now with the Lord.

With FAITH you can HOPE. With HOPE you give LOVE. May this book bring you help so you can help those you love.

PREFACE

Eighteen years ago I was a married mother of two, selling insurance and making and selling handcrafts. Along came a divorce, and I learned that life is a journey; you walk a path of stepping-stones. God puts each stone there, and you need to step on every one. I thought at that time that life could not get rougher; I was wrong.

Three years later I met my angel sent from God. My husband, Lynnay, was given to me, and he taught me that I could be anyone I chose to be, do anything I set my mind to do, and have faith that I wasn't walking this path alone.

In 1988 my oldest daughter, Michelle, was diagnosed with non-Hodgkin's lymphoma. My life changed forever. I learned that those stones along the path are God's way of keeping us from drowning. I walked each stone by just doing what needed to be done. Shelly died after eighteen months of trying to live. The morning after Shell died, my other daughter, Kim, said to me, "Now what do we do?" A great question, because our lives had been totally wrapped up in trying to help Shelly live. The only thing that came to my mind was to get our hair done. It sounded so simple. Life must and does go on.

Up until Shell died, I had only had six people close to me die. My grandmother and grandfather on my mom's side, my granddad on Dad's side, my great-aunt on Mom's side, and two good friends died the same year as Shell. Considering I was forty years old, that wasn't too bad. It was a blessing because God knew I had this incredible fear of dying. I couldn't even read the last chapter in the Bible because I was afraid of "endings." He would soon change that fear.

Shortly after Shell died I was asked by her doctor to sit on the Board of Directors for LifeCore, a new foundation that was starting up. LifeCore was going to help others that were facing bone marrow transplants. It was a new beginning because instead of trying to deal with what had happened to Shelly, I was able to help others face the same stones I had faced. My knowledge of the insurance industry, after fourteen years of working in all aspects of it, helped me to look at the money issues of transplants from a different perspective. Through LifeCore, I got involved with the National Marrow Donor Program®. My story went like this: Mother loses daughter. Mother gets involved in local group, LifeCore, to help others. Mother meets big national group, National Marrow Donor Program®. Mother is asked to work for LifeSavers, a group out of California, which is ultimately taken over by the big national program, National Marrow Donor Program®. Mother lasts six months with big group and gets laid off due to lack of funding. Mother goes back to LifeCore and helps patients and families around the U.S. raise money for transplants and find donors so patients can have those transplants.

I need to bring you up to date on what was going on in my personal life during that time. I got out of the insurance industry; it was too negative. I got my license to sell real estate and sold houses while continuing to work with transplant patients. My dad was given six months to live after being diagnosed with pancreatic cancer. He died after nine months. My mother died in a fire two years later. Lynnay kept me going on. He kept me involved with the patients and families I had been helping.

Then, while at a spring conference for the National Marrow Donor Program®, I received a phone call from home that Lynnay had died of an aortic aneurysm. I flew home to a changed life. In six years I had had to say good-bye to two best friends, my grandma, grandpa, mother, father, husband, and daughter. I was numb.

I turned to work and found that I could no longer face those patients who were trying so hard to live. I stayed in my office and did paperwork from the sidelines. I was trying to move into the new home Lynnay and I had purchased but he never saw completed. My life was so full of family and friends helping me; I was unable to do anything but just go on. I finally made the decision that I had to get away from my patients because my life was too full of dying.

A year later, after many of those stones to step on, God blessed me with a great gift. Lynnay's best friend and I fell in love. We were married, and Ron has become my "other half." God took a terrible loss and gave me a blessing. I have learned through Ron that God wants each of us to have someone that is "our own special person" here on earth to walk the walk with. Two years later, after still receiving phone calls in the night from people needing help with raising money, I started writing a book that Lynnay and I had discussed—about how an individual having to pay medical bills could raise money. Ron supported me by not pushing, and that is probably why it has taken so long to write. Shelly's father, Rick, has said I have finally found something I can do that puts all the things I have learned along this path to good use.

Now I work for a genetic testing lab out of Dallas, Texas. I sell HLA tests (the blood test that a donor needs to take before he or she can be listed on the National Registry to become a volunteer marrow donor for someone that needs a bone marrow transplant). I work with blood centers all over the U.S., helping to develop programs to find volunteer marrow donors. I help them raise money to pay for all this testing. My walk along this path has given me the wonderful gift of meeting and loving so many strong families. When they walk this path, many of them don't realize they are strong. They are just doing what needs to be done. Someday, looking back, they will see how tough it really was and how much they have learned. I think God plans it that way.

My path has blessed me with so many that have added to this book. My daughter Kim has grown up through all of this. I look at her and see that even at a young age, paths are not easy. A year after Shell died, Kim was at college and contracted a virus that attacked her pancreas; she was diagnosed with diabetes. I have watched her give herself four insulin shots a day and change her entire lifestyle to cope with yet another medical stone in the path of life. She now tries to educate others on how to live with diabetes. She has grown into a beautiful lady that Shelly would have been so proud of, and I marvel at all that she has become.

My grandson, Christopher, is Shelly's son. His father, Tom, has done such a great job raising him. He wasn't a year old when Shelly was diagnosed; he took his first steps in the halls of the Fred Hutchinson Cancer Center while Shelly was having a bone marrow transplant. He turned fourteen on September 26, 2000, and he is another gift from God. When he was little, I used to tell him he was perfect, and he would tell me it was because he was made by an angel. I could not imagine life without him.

Every book is written not just by the author, but by those who come into our lives. Dr. Robert Schuller, founder and senior pastor of the Crystal Cathedral in Garden Grove, California, is one such person. Through his television ministry and the many books he has written, he gives me the faith that God is a positive God, that God wants me happy, and that I truly can turn my hurt into a halo.

Zig Ziglar, internationally acclaimed speaker, author and sales authority, taught me that I must reach for the top; anything less is not what God wants for me.

Oprah Winfrey continues to speak to my heart. We are not the only ones walking a particular walk. Nothing is new here on earth. We are all here to help others. She has touched my spirit and given me the courage to speak out as she does to try to give others a road map for their journey.

My family has not always been easy to live with, but through everything they have always supported me. I pushed my family and friends a bit far when I decided a major fund-raiser for our local foundation was going to involve four huge parking lot garage sales all on the same day in three different towns. But they still hung in there. That is what families and friends are for.

My friend, boss, and soul sister is Tami Brown. Ten years ago she came to Oregon from California to try to get the money LifeCore had raised. Her boss from LifeSavers had met me at a National Marrow Donor Program® council meeting that was being held just five miles from my home in Bend, Oregon. He sent Tami to get LifeCore's money for their organization. I wouldn't give it to her, but they hired me, and our friendship has brought us over so many "stones." We have twisted and turned on this path together. But God really brought us together for a reason. There are days that we question what that reason is, but together we face whatever the transplant world hands us.

Ron is my earthly strength. Without him I never would have completed this book. I never would have picked up the phone book and called Shelley Blumberg, my editor and new friend.

Jeff Leeland was put in front of me for two years before I finally called him. His organization, The Sparrow Foundation, helps kids help kids facing medical problems. Without his help and the folks from Multnomah Publishers, I would not have gotten this book completed. My gratitude is overwhelming.

People hearing my story tell me I am a strong lady. I, like the patients and families I work with, don't think so. I am just doing what a mother does. I am just doing what needs to be done.

ONE

GETTING STARTED:

THE BASICS

First we must discuss what I call "The Realities." As much as I would like to tell you there are organizations or even individuals that will hand you two or three hundred thousand dollars to take care of all of your needs, the reality is, this will just not happen. Since I have been "looking for money," I have never been handed large sums for one specific person. The largest single donation I have received for an individual was $4,000. While this was very generous, it was just "a drop in the bucket" for what we needed.

I would like to be able to tell you everything will come out just fine and you will not have any problems. The reality is you are in the midst of one of the most confusing and overwhelming challenges you will ever face. Know, however, that there is help. You just need to reach out and take it.

You Have to Find Your Own

I have received many requests from individuals asking for help and asking for information about where they can receive help. The reality is, in most cases, you have to find your own. There are ways to go about this, and many people have been very successful in finding the funds they needed. However, you have to be creative, tenacious, and willing to step out of your comfort zone and do what is, in many cases, out of the ordinary.

This book will outline different avenues for finding the resources you require.

GATHER YOUR TOOLS

When the time comes and you realize you are facing the monumental task of getting through this, there are certain tools that will help. The necessity of many different directions coming together to accomplish one goal—getting the patient well—will require you and everyone around you to become organized. The following is your "school supply list" for the education you are about to receive. It will help keep things where you can find them.

• *A three-ring binder loaded with paper and lots of plastic pocket sheets*

Organize yourself so you know where you are and where you are going. You will want to know when you get there! Keep everything in this book. This binder will serve as your catchall. Keep track of important phone numbers: where the kids are staying this week, the phone number of the doctor who did something last week but wasn't your regular doctor, the person's name at the newspaper who has been asking to talk to you and you told him, "After I find out what is happening." Keep the directions to the treatment center in here if you have never been there before. All insurance papers and bills that have been opened go in this book. Unopened bills go in "The BOX," which will be discussed in chapter 4. Keep everything that pertains to your journey.

In a later chapter, I will discuss tax-deductible items. Keep your mileage and medically related expenses not covered by insurance in your notebook. You might be able to declare these items as a tax deduction. It is better to keep everything and then throw out what isn't needed. You never know when you will need to find something, and you'll most likely have to look for it at the least opportune time. Keep this notebook close.

• *The little spiral notebook*

Keep this with you at all times. When someone comes up and asks if there is anything they can do to help, say, "Not right now, but let me write your name and phone number down in my little book, and when the time comes I will call. Thank you so much for offering!" You just can't remember everything and everyone. Write down all your contacts; they are vital. Keep these lists handy. In my later days of helping to raise funds for patients, I would hand out as many as five or six of these little books to family and friends of the patient so they could keep track of "important contacts." You need help, so keep track of these wonderful friends.

• *Your insurance and medical papers*

Your insurance and medical papers are vital. Read chapter 4, "Setting up Your Records," and compile everything you need to keep track of your costs.

The "BOX." Chapter 4 will tell you what this is for.

• *Know why you need to raise funds*

Be clear about what your needs are. You have options as to where the funds you raise must go. I have seen patients and families go to the public asking for donations to test for bone marrow donors. The cost averages $45 per test. I know of a community that raised $20,000 to test its citizens. After all the tests were completed, it was determined the patient didn't have enough insurance or money to enter the transplant center. However, little Johnny's brother was going to be the donor the entire time. The moral? They didn't need to raise funds for donor testing! They didn't have enough money to get plane tickets to travel to Minnesota for the treatment!

Everyone must remember there are five elements to this whole process:

1. The patient
2. who has a disease
3. and needs a treatment,
4. in some cases requires a donor,
5. always requires money.

If you take away one element, you can't have any of them. It is the old saying, "Which comes first, the chicken or the egg?" If you have already found your donor and your insurance will pay the donor costs, then don't go to the public raising funds for donor testing—especially if you don't have enough insurance coverage to cover the treatment itself. Ask your doctor how much post-treatment costs will be. The average out of pocket (i.e., after insurance payments) cost to the patients I surveyed was $28,000, and this was in 1994.

Determine the many "other" costs related to your treatment (i.e., travel, wages lost, anything that will not be paid by insurance). Make sure you ask for the "right" amount for the right reasons.

ASKING FOR HELP, THEN ACCEPTING IT

When I was working with patients and families, the biggest hurdle I had was to get them to ask for help. The second was getting them to accept it. It is very difficult to lay yourself out for the public and let them know you need help. However, if we all stop and think about it, every one of us could be in the same position. The reality here is, very few individuals are prepared to pay bills the size of medical costs. "Normal" medical costs are high, but major medical costs are astronomical. Why do you think they call it "major"?

Keep in mind that the reality of trying to find such enormous funding is a daunting task. Rule one of obtaining funding or even (medically) getting through what you are facing is:

You can't do it alone. Don't even try. It does not work!

You must take this to heart. All through this book I will be referring to examples of using the resources available to you. One major resource we all have is the people around us. These people will help you, instruct you, pick you up, and keep you going. Don't count anyone out. You as the patient have got to spend your time getting well. Let others help where they can.

You Need to Take Drastic Steps

Finding an approach to get started is the first step. You must first realize you need to take drastic steps. Ask yourself: What things must I do? Hopefully this book will give you a direction. The approach you take will determine what direction to take. In any case, you are about to embark on a journey. Think about it: Many people can't figure out how to make it from paycheck to paycheck. Being faced with a bill of one or two hundred thousand dollars will stop you cold.

The problem is compounded by the fact that hospitals are now looking at "ability to pay" before you are even able to obtain treatment. In everyday terms: "If you don't have the money, you don't receive treatment." My daughter said of a young man facing a bone marrow transplant, "If Chris is willing to go through what I just went through, he shouldn't have to worry about money." The reality is that someone has to worry about the costs. Hospitals cannot afford to take care of everyone for nothing. So it is up to us to pay.

Ask for What You Need — No More, No Less

If you are reading this, you are no doubt in the process of "looking for money." Your first step is finding out how much. In a later chapter I will talk about what it takes to come up with a price. If you are going out to the public to ask for help, it is imperative that you ask for what you need—no more, no less. People want to know exactly what they are spending their money on and how much it costs. Being a nice person with a disease and needing help isn't enough. You must be able to give specifics. Be sure to read chapter 5 thoroughly before you start out.

WHO NEEDS HELP MORE?

Another reality in fund-raising for medical needs is the question of age. As difficult as it is to say, it is much easier to raise money for a child than for an adult. I have done a lot for both the young and the old. Presenting the case and gaining support is the key to a successful fund-raising campaign. The public is prepared to help the adorable little blue-eyed, blond, curly-haired three-year-old, no questions asked. Ask them to help a forty-year-old truck driver, and you have to tell them why.

Present your case. The truck driver has worked all his life for the same company, and they just went out of business. The man has just started out on his own and doesn't have health insurance set up yet. He has three children and a wife who depend on him. His wife works full time, but without him on the road, they can't feed the family let alone pay medical bills. Who needs help more: the child that has a mom and dad both working with medical insurance that just doesn't pay enough, or the truck driver who is supporting an entire family?

Take the time to think about why people would want to help you. Then go to the public and ask for help, emphasizing why they should support your cause. It's hard to plead a case for yourself, but the alternative is not receiving help.

THIS IS WHERE YOU ARE. ACCEPT IT!

When you accept the fact that you need help and you need it now, you are on the road to success. Wishing away what is going on won't change your situation. Getting angry with yourself and everyone around you will not help. Not taking a positive step in the direction you need to go will not help you solve your problem.

Wally Amos of Uncle Noname Cookie Company fame put it this way: "This is the way it is, and the course of events now depends entirely on me. I can turn this into lemonade, or I can let it sour my whole life. I could only deal with my problem once I separated my emotions from the facts. Once I did that, I gained control of my situation and could make the necessary moves to resolve it."

At some point every patient and family feels they have lost control. Well, you have! Accept it and move on. Control those things you can. The most successful fund-raising campaigns out there are done by the people who have decided: "This is the only thing I have any control over, and I am going to do it the best I can!" Accept where you are, and do something positive to move on.

Just do it. Do anything, but do something!

THE REALITY OF LEARNING

Every experience you have in life is an opportunity to learn something. Looking back at Shell's disease and the effects it had on my family and my entire life, I have learned a valuable lesson: God gives us the hills *and* the valleys. If we never had valleys to learn from, we wouldn't appreciate the hills. When you have the opportunity to work with others, listen to them. When you don't know what to do or which way to proceed, ask questions of others. At the end of this experience you will be amazed at all you have learned. You will marvel at how many people will come out and help you, how many really wanted to help and just needed to be asked.

When I first started working in the bone marrow transplant field, I asked Dave Frohnmayer, then Attorney General of the State of Oregon, and Admiral Zumwalt, former Commander of the Joint Chiefs of Staff, (both then on the Board of Directors of the National

Marrow Donor Program® and leaders in fighting the diseases that struck their own children) if they knew anything about the diseases when their children had become sick. They both responded, "Not a thing."

This taught me a great deal. These men have done incredible things for the medical community that treats patients with the diseases their families faced. They are now leaders to whom people from all over the world turn for help. The way you learn is by walking the walk. You will have the opportunity to learn much in the next few months of your life. At each step ask, "What is this teaching me?" I always said, "This is just another stepping-stone to building character." I have to admit; there were times when I was "charactered" out. Learn from all that is happening. Good or bad, you will have a whole new outlook on life.

STAY POSITIVE!

There will be times when you feel it is just too much. Too much of everything. Shelly, who was one of our social butterflies, used to get so tired of everyone coming to visit her. She said she felt like a monkey in a zoo. The media can, in its effort to help you raise money or get the story, become a real problem. Well-meaning friends will call and come over at bad times. The doctors will explain everything so many times without saying anything you understand. You will feel sick and ugly and not want anyone to see you, let alone talk to you.

As a family member you will wonder if anyone ever thinks about what you are going through instead of just the patient. All these things are normal—if anything can be considered normal at this time of your life. We all have the choice of having a good day or a bad day. Choose to find the good and the beauty in each situation that comes up. Try to look beyond where you are at that moment.

The reality is, God wants you to have the best there is. He wants you to be happy. Keep a positive outlook on life, no matter what happens! Visualize yourself getting better, raising the money you need, keeping a positive outlook. Having faith means believing in those things we can't see. One of my patients visualized hunting for elk when he completed his bone marrow transplant. That is what he held on to while in the transplant center. When he was released from the center, he went hunting and got that elk.

Whatever or whoever helps you to keep a positive outlook is what you need to hold on to while walking through this minefield. Try to keep your chin up and do whatever you can. Every step you take is one step closer to completing this journey.

ASSESS WHAT

YOU HAVE

By assessing what kind of resources you have, you will be better able to make the correct choices regarding the direction you need to follow in obtaining the funds for your medical costs. The charts at the end of this chapter are examples of ways to handle these kinds of assessments. You will be filling out a financial report, listing all the resources you currently have.

RESOURCE NUMBER 1:
HEALTH INSURANCE

The first question you need to ask is: "Do I have health insurance that will cover what I need to have done?" Chapter 3 will discuss health insurance in great detail, but for now just look at the policy and find out if it covers your disease; if so, determine the limits. Remember, when figuring how much insurance you have, you must determine what it doesn't cover and how much you will have to pay.

What is your deductible, and what is your co-pay amount? The co-pay amount is the percentage of the bill that insurance doesn't cover. Also, figure in what the insurance company refers to as the "reasonable and customary costs." Most companies will only pay reasonable and customary costs for any given procedure, appointment, whatever. If your doctor charges $75 for an X-ray and the insurance company will pay only $50, you will have to pay the difference plus your percentage of the co-pay.

Another thing to look out for is what the industry now refers to as "preferred providers"—doctors and/or facilities that the insurance company works with directly. These providers have contracted to accept insurance/co-pay amounts that have been established as reasonable and customary. If, for example, that amount is $1,000 and the physician/lab/facility bill is $1,200, the amount the insurance will pay is $1,000 of the $1,200. I have seen doctors go back and bill the patient the additional $200 not paid by the insurance company. Questions you must ask:

- Do I have coverage for my particular treatment/disease?
- How much?
- What is my deductible?
- What is the co-payment?
- Are my doctors (remember you have more than one) "preferred providers"?

If you do not have health insurance at this time because you left your job or because your coverage under a group plan has for some reason expired, you might be covered by the Consolidated Omnibus Budget Reconciliation Act of 1985 (COBRA). The act requires most employers who sponsor group health plans to offer employees and their families the opportunity to temporarily extend health coverage at group rates. Qualifying events are:

1. termination of your services for any reason except gross misconduct,
2. reduction of your hours.

There are a number of other events that can qualify you for the COBRA plan. Just know that if you are a patient and were laid off work due to your illness and your health insurance coverage was cancelled, this act gives you the right to continue coverage for eighteen months. You still need to pay the premiums, but you will have coverage.

RESOURCE NUMBER 2:
FAMILY FUNDS/PERSONAL RESOURCES

List all your assets as far as bank account balances. It is important to realize that if, in the future, it is determined that you need to go to the public for funds, they will want to know if you have money and are paying for everything you can afford to pay for.

I refer to this category as the "family funds." I use the term *family* because the public looks to extended family members as well as immediate family members for support. For example, a sick child's mother and father might not have any money, but the child's grandfather may be a well-known, affluent individual. The public will ask what the grandfather is doing to help and question why he doesn't pay for the treatment. Remember, I didn't say this was going to be easy. Again, when you go to the public, you must remember they will most always ask hard questions. Make sure you are doing everything you can do before you ask others to step in and help.

RESOURCE NUMBER 3:
STATE AND FEDERAL PROGRAMS

To qualify for any state or federal programs, such as Medicare and Supplemental Security Income, you need to go to your local Social Service Department in your county or state offices. Guidelines will tell you: "To qualify for disability from Social Security, you must have a physical or mental impairment that is expected to keep you from doing any 'substantial' work for at least a year," or you must have a condition that is "expected to result in your death."

Be prepared to lay your life out on a piece of paper. Face this challenge as positively as you can. You will meet many people along your journey. Some are wonderful, and some are very busy. Document everything — every person you talk to, every piece of paper you send, EVERYTHING. It is a long and tedious road. You will have to step on every stone, sometimes many times, before you will reach the end.

While forms often vary, you can expect at least a six-page questionnaire. This is just the start. As you progress down the road, you will have a form handed or mailed to you at every turn. You will need birth certificates, health and life insurance policies, evaluations, doctors' reports, bank statements, and W-2 forms. It is always helpful to copy any required documents you need to produce because they will want copies for their files. Forms are a way of life; if you are missing one, it can slow things to a standstill. Again, be prepared. It is not unusual to have to fill out seventy-five to one hundred different forms.

Also prepare for *time*. The Social Security Division does not work fast. It often turns people down two or three times before finally accepting their claim. If you are turned down the first time but feel you have a good claim, don't give up. Keep trying.

I will remind you of this in a later chapter, but I must interject something here. It is a very important item: *If you are applying for assistance from SSI and (1) you receive any funds from outside fundraising and (2) they are in the name of the person filing the SSI claim, the amount collected can be counted as ordinary income and will affect the amount of money you might be able to receive from SSI.* Be very careful how any money raised is given to the patient.

State medical insurance programs can be easier to qualify for, but you need to check with your particular state and find out if you fit their guidelines.

RESOURCE NUMBER 4:
GRANTS AND SPECIAL AWARDS

Grants and special awards *are* awarded. But first you need to apply and see if you will be accepted. One patient I worked with went to her employer and explained her problem. After some research she was told her company had an employee emergency fund and she qualified for a special one-time check for $1,000. The company also sponsored and paid for a bone marrow donor testing session through the local Red Cross. Her fellow workers even divided up their vacation time and took one less day themselves, essentially working one day for her so she wouldn't have to lose valuable income.

There are many different ways you can find help if you just ask. Go to your boss or a human resources person; ask if there might be some help. Many employers and fellow workers come up with innovative ways of finding money to help their coworkers—patients and their families. We will talk more about this in chapter 6.

Churches have been known to help, not only by giving money via special offerings, but also by providing living accommodations or travel arrangements for members of the family who do not live close. Again, you need to step out of that comfort zone and ask for help.

A major point here is, if you go and ask for help, be ready to ask for specific items—money, a ride to another city, a plane ticket, whatever you might need. One family asked for help because they didn't have any firewood; the father was having a transplant and had been in the hospital for two months. The local Lions Club went out and cut, split, and stacked enough wood for the entire winter. Ask. Let your needs be known. You just never know where help will come from.

RESOURCE NUMBER 5:
CHARITIES, GROUPS, AND ORGANIZATIONS

Some specific nonprofit organizations have one-time grants for patients with a disease that is covered by their program. One state organization gives people with leukemia $500 to help with bills. Another organization will pay for all disease-related travel expenses. The best thing to do when faced with a particular disease is to find out if there is a support group that helps people with your type of problem. Contact the group and ask what kind of services it offers.

The first time you call a particular group you might not get the most knowledgeable person on the phone. Ask to speak with the CEO, Executive Director, or the person in charge. If you live in a small community, you might have to call the state office. An example is the American Cancer Society. If you live in a small town, chances are you will reach a volunteer answering the phone. Now while that person is a very valuable person to the local organization, he or she might not know all the different programs offered through state and national chapters. Always go to the top.

Keep trying until you feel you have exhausted all the avenues and have all the answers you need. When Shelly asked the local Cancer Society what they offered, they said they could drive her back and forth to her chemo treatments and provided used wigs. That was all! We all know the Cancer Society offers more than that. We didn't know to keep asking.

RESOURCE NUMBER 6:
CLINICAL TRIALS

Ask the doctor, hospital, or transplant center if there are any clinical trials being conducted for your treatment. Sometimes you can get on a special program, and the cost can be reduced or even free. These bonuses are few and far between, but are well worth looking into.

RESOURCE NUMBER 7:
ASK FOR A "DEAL"

When facing a large medical expense, it is not unusual to go directly to the health-care provider and ask for a "deal." Some doctors will adjust their fees. Some hospitals will negotiate bills. Wherever there is a possible way to save money, ask for it. Insurance companies do it all the time. If you do not have an insurance company representing you, then represent yourself.

A group I worked with once raised a large amount of money and had it in a special account set aside for a specific patient. The transplant hospital said the patient could not have the transplant until we paid the entire bill. They hadn't done a thing yet, and they wanted us to pay the bill up front! We told them no way. The bank sent a verification of funds in the account. The doctor in charge of this patient called the hospital and told them they would be paid as they billed. We could, therefore, review the bills and pay accordingly. As it turned out, the bank account holding the money made about $1,000 in interest, and we discovered that the hospital had made a $6,000 error in the billing. If we had paid in advance, the hospital would have gotten the interest and we would not have caught the $6,000 error. Don't be afraid to stand up for yourself.

Look to all the different kinds of help you already have. You have your personal resources, health insurance, state and federal programs, charities and organizations. Make a list and know where you stand going into this money-finding adventure. Be sure to keep everything in writing in your notebook so you don't have to go back and figure everything again when someone asks for something.

The following is an example of an actual letter one of my patients and I put together. After sending out this information, we were both pleasantly surprised at the number of doctors — not office managers or account reps, but doctors! — who called and/or wrote thanking her for this information. One of her doctors responded by making a reasonable decision about the bill, allowing them to go on without the outstanding debts hanging over both of them. He took what the insurance company paid and wrote off the rest of the bill. He said if more patients would discuss their bills like this, financial problems could be resolved more often. Admittedly, some doctors never responded after numerous pleas, but one doctor willing to help is better than none. You must ASK!

From: Susie Patient   Date: August 1, 1995
111 NW Street
Town, USA 0000
111-111-1111
Subject: Payment of Outstanding Bills
To Whom It May Concern:

This letter is to advise you of my financial ability to pay my outstanding bill with you. I have non-Hodgkin's lymphoma. I was diagnosed March 1995. I have tried to pay each bill each month. My insurance is with ABC Insurance Company. They have paid on most of the bills. My problem is that I had a $500 deductible, and they only pay 80% of "reasonable and customary" expenses. As I am finding out, your billings sometimes do NOT come under "reasonable and customary." This leaves me with an outstanding bill. In the past I have been able to pay you each month. I think if you look into my records you will find this to be true.

    This now brings me to my latest problem. I am currently, and have been, working as a waitress at the Food Restaurant since August of 1989. My boss has been great about working around my schedule of medical appointments. I was scheduled for a bone marrow transplant in November of this year. My insurance company has now said I cannot have one until June of 1996 because of a waiting period in the policy. Both of my doctors have written to them, and we are waiting for them to reverse their decision. Until that time I need to have ongoing chemotherapy in a town 130 miles away from home. Not only does this cause me to be off work because of travel time, but I am finding that the chemo makes me too sick to work. I am, however, working a couple days a week. This does not cover my living expenses, let alone the medical bills I am faced with. I have applied to every state and federal agency to obtain help, but you have to be destitute before they will even talk to you. Because I have a job and am buying a home, they say I do not qualify.

This letter is to request that you would please do two things: 1) Look to my current bills and see if you can either make an adjustment or write off the balance due; 2) take what the insurance company pays you as reasonable and customary and write off the balance. I do not like having to ask, but I am unable to do anything else.

I have enclosed certain documentation of my financial position. If you need further information please feel free to call. I would like to have your answer in writing so I can keep it with my medical bills. Please let me know by the end of this month before my next set of bills comes in. This has been a very confusing time for me. If you cannot do as I have asked, could you please give some suggestions on what other options I might have?

Thank you,

Susie Patient

Outstanding Medical Bills—Provider		
	ACCOUNT NUMBER	AMOUNT
Med. Clinic	001 00015	$1,705.00
Dr. Jones	03845	54.00
Pathology Lab	001 05496	27.00
Pathology Lab	05499	83.00
Radiology Lab	01101-000012549	121.00
Dr. Brown		500.09
Hospital	1 30755	2,258.80
Hospital	2 309236	143.00
Hospital	3 24445	190.21
Hospital	4 289955	454.00
University Hospital	1333996	8,500.00
	TOTAL:	$14,036.10

MONTHLY BILLS	PROVIDER	TYPE OF PAYMENT	AMOUNT
Mortgage	Bank of America	Monthly	$617.00
Phone	AT&T	Average	87.00
Electric	Pacific Power	Average	79.00
Cable		Average	20.40
Water		Average	20.00
Garbage		Average	18.35
Health Insurance		Average	79.40
		Total	$921.15

REGULAR MONTHLY PAYMENTS			
MISC. BILLS	TOTAL OWED	BILLING CYCLE	MONTHLY PAYMENT
Visa	4,085.93	Monthly	$103.00
Discover	744.93	Monthly	20.00
Car Insurance	648.00	Every 6 mo.	108.00
Property Taxes	1,913.90	Annually	160.00
		TOTAL MONTHLY PAYMENT:	$288.00

SOURCE OF INCOME	TYPE OF INCOME	AMOUNT
Wages	Average Take Home	$178.00
Tips	Average	120.00
Son	Room & Board	200.00
Daughter	Room & Board	200.00
	TOTAL MONTHLY INCOME	$698.00

THREE

WORKING WITH YOUR INSURANCE COMPANY

Insurance companies around the country are finally acknowledging that many treatments called experimental in the past are now considered "state of the art" treatment. Their views on what is covered are broadening in some areas and shrinking in others. Dealing with insurance companies can be very tricky, and you need to approach this job with particular care. I always tell families to approach their insurance company as they would a miserly rich relative. The relative loves you and wants the best, but knowing you need money from them, they are ready for the hit. It's not that they don't want to give you any money; they just want to make sure they don't need to pay for anything you don't *really* need.

We need to talk briefly about the different kinds of insurance companies and how they handle claims. There are private insurers, HMOs, PPOs, MEWAs — the list goes on forever. You, as the patient or the person handling the insurance claims, must examine the policy and start asking questions. Call the company and find out who will handle your case. Have the first page of your policy, called the Declaration Page, with you. This tells you what coverage you have, the deductibles, effective date, and so on.

Look for any endorsements—anything that is added to your policy to make it different from the company's original contract. These endorsements can result in increased or decreased coverage.

Many times this is where it states what kind of prescription drug benefits you have and/or which preexisting conditions are not covered.

The Summary of Benefits lists deductibles, lifetime limits and limitations on the policy. Preexisting conditions should be approached with extreme caution. If you purchased your policy and knew about or had been treated for your condition and the company has listed it as a preexisting condition (or the company finds out you had a problem before they wrote the policy), they might not cover it at all or might put a waiting period on the treatment for that particular problem.

New laws governing insurance policies and coverage are happening everyday. Coverage is being extended and cut back. Try to stay on top of what is happening. If you feel totally out of your league, call your insurance agent and ask for help. Other avenues include going to your human resources director at work or calling your insurance company directly and asking if any new laws have been passed to help you.

PREADMISSION NOTIFICATION

If you are facing a hospital stay, you need to notify your insurance company. In most cases the hospital or doctor will handle this for you. However, you should double-check and make sure the hospital has verified preadmission. By now you should have established a healthy relationship with your insurance claim representative, so call and make sure everything is in place for the company's records, and let the rep know that you are going into the hospital and claims will be coming in. Some insurance companies will accept a phone call; others need written confirmation. Again, every company is different, so check with your rep and make sure you are doing what needs to be done.

It is always difficult to make sure you have covered all the bases, but it is better to err on the side of being overzealous than not making a concentrated effort to make sure everything is taken care of. Extra costs pop up all the time. In the case of transplants, a cost that very often slips through the cracks is that of searching for a donor. Some insurance companies will pay for the search and then not pay the donor costs. Check with your doctor or the medical accounting office and make sure you are aware of what you will need to have covered.

If you are lucky enough to have what is called a "Cancer Care" or "Intensive Care" policy, you will want to make sure you are paid what you have coming. One company has underwriting rules that state if you are not in intensive care when the policy is *written*, you can get their policy. If you face a transplant, it would be very wise to verify this aspect of your policy; it is not unusual to be in intensive care through these procedures. Bone marrow transplants are considered intensive care by some policies. Such a policy would cover the whole time you are in the transplant center. The insurance agent who wrote the policy usually pays the claim through the company, and the agent would be the one to file your claim for you. The money you receive is yours to do with as you see fit. It can be a great help paying for travel, deductibles, or whatever.

AUTOMATED ANSWERING SYSTEMS

We need to talk just a moment about these wonderful inventions. Although answering machines have been around for years, the insurance industry has taken the concept to new lengths. You need to be prepared. Plan ahead. Basic rules are:

- Set aside plenty of time. If you get right through the first time, which is rare, it is still time consuming.
- Always have a piece of paper and pencil with you. You will need to keep track of what numbers to push relevant to what you want.

- Always have your three-ring binder with you. Open it to your insurance page, where your policy number and any other important names or numbers are.
- If you know your claims rep, make sure you ask for the direct extension number to cut through all the other options.
- Be prepared to call back because most of the time you will get through to your rep and find a "voice mail box" telling you to leave a detailed message. Go ahead and leave a message, and then be prepared to call back if the message goes unanswered. After you hang up, make sure you leave your paper, pencil and notebook by the phone, so if and when the rep calls back you can have everything ready.
- Be specific as to why you are calling. Know what you need and how they can help.
- Telephone calls can be expensive; always ask for 800 numbers.
- Document the date you are calling, to whom you talked, and the details of the conversation as best you can.
- Put everything in your binder so you can refer to it the next time you need to speak with the company.

INSURANCE DISPUTES

Twenty to thirty percent of all claims are lost, denied, or delayed pending further work. With increased electronic billing, there are more denials. Don't just assume a denied claim is correct. Don't trust too easily. Question and make sure you understand why a claim is not being paid. Many times a simple phone call can clear up a misunderstanding or error. Always question.

When a claim is denied, make sure you are aware of what is happening out there in the marketplace regarding your treatment. In the case of bone marrow transplants, some companies are still saying that they are experimental; therefore they do not need to pay.

Recent court rulings can be used to effectively reverse the company's decision. Be aware and know the rules of the game. It is the only way you can play fairly and ultimately win.

Read your policy. It is a contract between you and your insurance carrier, and the carrier must live up to it. Highlight anything you feel has to do with your particular claim and/or problem. Here are some rules to follow when dealing with your insurance company.

- The squeaky wheel gets the grease. Everyone needs to know you at the insurance company.
- Document, document, document. Go back and reconstruct what has happened since the beginning.
- Keep track of all phone calls made—to whom you spoke and when.
- Ask if there is anyone else you should speak to.
- Keep copies of everything you send out.
- Keep everything you receive. Try to keep all this in chronological order for easy access.

- Tell them:
  - your problem;
  - what you want;
  - what you are going to do if you do not hear from them;
  - what you will do based on all the evidence you have compiled.

- Find out:
  - the name of the person handling the denial;
  - the phone number and extension to reach them;
  - if there is anyone the representative answers to and, if so, that name and phone number;

- the address you can write to directly to reach your rep;
- a fax number;
- the rep's suggestions for handling your particular problem.

- Establish a friendship with the person handling the denial. He/she can really help you. *Be polite, no matter what.*
  - Talk to your insurance agent and ask these questions:
    - When you bought the policy, were there any questions of coverage that would indicate that your problem would not be covered?
    - Did the agent make any claims about the policy that you are now questioning?
    - Can the agent go to the company for you?
      The agent might say it is out of the question, but an agent has to be able to believe in the product. The company knows this, and in some cases an agent does carry weight with the company. Remember, that agent would not get a commission if you had not bought the policy from him/her. That agent is your representative.
    - Why is coverage being denied or modified? Ask! Put him/her on the spot. Let the agent explain to you if he/she can.

- Keep together and bring all pertinent information dealing with your policy, including:
  - payment records of how and the amount you paid.
  - checkbooks, premium notices, statements, etcetera.
  - statements of insurance payments made in your behalf.
  - copies of highlighted pertinent information from your contract (policy). When you send your letters, be sure to enclose the copies of anything that proves your case.
  - any change of coverage notifications from the company (addendums).

- list of any changes and dates they took place, such as:
    a. taking a person off the policy;
    b. change in the deductible;
    c. going from a group to an individual plan.

- Itemize everything, and take copies of your statements showing that a certain claim was paid before, and attach the statements to your list. Then ask why are they saying it is not covered now.
- Contact organizations such as the National Marrow Donor Program® and the National Institute of Health to get any statistical information backing up whatever you need to prove your case.
- Compile your "case." Put it all down on paper in a clear, concise order. Review it and make any additions or corrections. Point out what has changed about your situation and what is the same. Prove that you have not missed any payments and you are living up to your end of the contract. Point out that the insurance company is the one that is being questioned here.

- Put all the documented and itemized information into one letter. Send it to:
    - the head of the insurance company;
    - the Medical Director of the company;
    - the claims representative for the company;
    - your insurance agent;
    - the insurance commissioners of your state;
    - your attorney (if you have one);
    - your employer and/or the human resources office;
    - your union representative (if there is one).

- Be sure to list ("cc:") at the bottom of the page everyone to whom you are sending this letter, thus making everyone aware of who else knows about this. If you ever go to the media with your story, having done this will be helpful.

- The letter should include:
  - an initial positive statement or a compliment of some kind;
  - a clear statement of what you feel is wrong;
  - specific details or aspects of your complaint;
  - documented pertinent information.

- If you have read your policy and do not find anything referring to your particular problem, request that the company supply you with a specific ruling on its decision or action.

  For example: If the company tells you your treatment is experimental but you don't find any specific information on this, ask (1) why they are ruling this way, (2) on what are they basing their information, and (3) that they substantiate all their statements with data, just like you did.

- By sending copies of information from the insurance company and your records, you are giving the insurance commissioner and other parties the information they need to make a ruling. Make sure everyone knows you are looking at the entire picture. State that:
  - You will force this issue until you have been given the answers and are satisfied with the decision.
  - You have nothing to lose and feel you are being treated unfairly.
  - You need to know why they are changing the contract you purchased. Ask for answers to very specific questions: why they are not covering the treatment you thought was covered, why the procedure is considered experimental, why your rates have been raised, why they are canceling you, etc.

- The insurance company has a choice of convincing you they are correct, changing the unfair ruling, or changing the entire contract because it is unjust. If the insurance company states there is something in the contract that proves their point, then tell them the contract needs to be changed and you will fight them until it is.

Just a quick story: A patient was denied coverage because of a waiting period for transplants. The doctors wrote the insurance company, explained the case, and gave them figures showing it would cost a lot more to wait for the treatment, because the insurance company was paying for chemo and ongoing treatment for the patient. The company still refused to allow the transplant. The agent got involved in the problem and went to the company on behalf of the patient. The company explained that if the policy the insured had purchased allowed the company to make an exception, they would have, but because the waiting period requirement was stated in the contract, they could not change it just for her. It would mean changing the coverage for everyone. Therefore, they said, the patient would have to wait. The rest of the story is that the insurance company did, in fact, later change the contract. Now they have the right to make an exception for special cases on a case by case basis. It just goes to show that you *can* make a difference for others.

Send everything to the people you have listed. Give them a time frame in which you would like an answer. Make it a specific date (e.g., two weeks).

Time is of the essence. This is your life.

Tell them that. State that if you have not heard from them in two weeks, you will file a formal complaint with the insurance commissioner. During those two weeks, contact your insurance commissioner and find out how to file a claim. This will save time later.

Have them send you anything and everything they can on what you need to know and do.

If you do send in a claim, send a copy of it to the same people you sent the original letter, as well as a copy to your congressmen, senators, and everyone else you can think of. Make sure everyone knows you are not giving up.

Once you have gone this far, call upon your special relationship with the insurance claims representative. Call once again and make sure there isn't anything else you can do to resolve this issue. Is there anyone else who could help you?

You Now Have Three Choices

1. If you still feel you are right after everything, take it to your attorney.
2. Drop it and seek help elsewhere.
3. Go to the media (more on that later).

Things to Keep in Mind

Customer representatives get calls from insureds all day long. They are on the firing line constantly. You might be the nicest person in the world, but if they just got off the phone with a real grouch, you are going to pay the price. I am not saying all reps are in foul moods, but many of them are. Try to keep yourself under control. Remember, you help pay their wages, and they are there to help you. These customer reps have no way of knowing you are an intelligent, rational person that honestly wants to do the right thing. They are going to place you with the rest of the screaming masses they deal with every day.

Some reps look at your situation like this:

- You bought their insurance policy.
- You should have known exactly what you were buying.
- You don't like the coverage, but that's what you have.

- They can't change the policy.
- They are just doing their job.
- So take it or leave it.

Other reps approach your problems like this:
- You bought the policy.
- They want you to understand it.
- They will explain why they aren't covering a specific item.
- They take pride in helping you to solve your problem.
- If the problem was a mistake on their part, they will correct it.
- They will make an effort to get any disputes taken care of as soon as possible.
- They want you to be a satisfied customer.

Approach all reps as if they will treat you the way the second kind does. The old saying is true: "You get back what you give." If you go in with a negative, angry attitude, that is what you will get back. Go to the rep and explain you are trying to understand all this and you need his/her help. If you truly find a rep that you can't work with, ask for a supervisor and get someone new working with you.

One medical claims advocate stated, "There is a vast difference between what insurance companies want to cover and what they should cover." You have to understand their language to get every dime they owe you. Remember:

If it is to be, it is up to me.

You are in control. You need to know your path so you can get what is coming to you. It will not just happen; you have to work for it.

FOUR

SETTING UP YOUR

RECORDS—CATCHALL

Your three-ring binder will serve as a catchall. Keep it with you wherever you go. You will be amazed by all you collect. If it is easier to have all your medical records in another book, then by all means do it. There are no rules in this game saying you can have only one book. Keep your catchall book with you at all times, and give the medical record or insurance book to the person handling your accounts.

The purpose of your three-ring binder is to free you from frantically searching for information when you aren't feeling well. Even if you don't put everything in the right order right away, at least you will have a starting place to find what you are looking for.

Setting up records (both medical bills and records you use in setting up a fund-raising campaign) can be a job that seems unnecessary. However, it will save you time, energy, and elevated stress levels if you will just take the time to do it.

As I have stated before, you need to know where you are before you can get to where you are going. Setting up complete and accurate records can and does save time as you walk through all the steps of this journey.

WHAT KIND OF INFORMATION?

List the following numbers at the front of your book for easy reference. They are numbers you will use continually. Also, you want to establish a relationship with the people you have to work with. Talking to the same person each time you call will save you a lot of time because you won't have to bring a new person up to date each time you have a problem.

TELEPHONE NUMBERS:

Doctor

Doctor's nurse's name

Hospital

Insurance company

Account rep handling your bill (number and extension)

Account rep handling your claim (number and extension)

Friends offering help

Volunteers helping with fund-raising campaign

MEDICAL NUMBERS:

Insurance policy number

Social Security

Medicaid/Medicare/any financial assistance program number

(Many times this is your Social Security Number.)

THE BOX

In many cases the patient is too sick to do a lot of things that need to be done. I have found it works well to designate a person to handle the money end of things. This person can be a spouse, although I don't recommend it. A spouse is often overwhelmed with the pressures of his or her loved one's medical treatments, being the primary caregiver to any children, and/or continuing to work so bills can be paid.

Having a person close to you who will take on the task of handling the bills will greatly help when problems come up. I will talk later in chapter 8 about friends and relatives accepting some of the burden. For now let's just give you some pointers.

Have one person (maybe two) handle the bills. This way the

insurance company and care providers will establish a relationship with this person and will know that they will follow through. Give this person a letter authorizing them to talk to the care providers and the insurance company on your behalf. This needs to be in writing and sent to all your accounts. This will save time so you won't have to be bothered every time something needs to be done.

Have a BOX devoted to anything pertaining to medical bills. When the mail comes in, all bills will be put in the BOX. The person handling the bills will be the one opening them. You will not have the problem of trying to figure out what was billed or not billed because of missing statements. It is very hard and confusing to try to reconstruct a billing statement if you don't have all the pieces.

I know this sounds rather scary, but I have told patients and their families not to open bills, because they can't pay them anyway. The bills have a tendency to create more stress. Don't, however, let the bills just sit unopened. Make sure the person handling them gets them in a timely manner.

This person will enter the bills in your notebook and keep track of what has been paid and what hasn't. Give them this book and have them read the chapters on setting up records and handling insurance companies.

MEDICAL RECORDS

There are some helpful tips you can put to use when setting up your three-ring binder. We are going to build you a book from start to finish. Just think of your binder as a book you are writing.

Use dividers to separate each of your bills (chapters). Put a table of contents in the front and list each creditor in alphabetical order. As you separate your bills, just stick them into the right chapter. Don't do anything other than "file" them in the correct place. After you have gotten them separated, go to each individual chapter and put each bill in chronological order. Pay close attention to the account number. Many places set up a new account number each time you go for service. This can cause confusion when trying to figure out what has been paid and what has not. If you have more than one account number for a particular creditor, separate each one by placing a piece of colored paper between each account. Be sure to write the account number on the "title page" (which should be on colored paper). Then separate and place in order of the oldest dated bill on the bottom, moving through time to the newest bill on the top. Once you have completed all the bills, punch holes in them and put them into the binder in order. At the beginning of each chapter have a "title page" with the provider's name, address, phone number, account number or numbers, the name of the doctor, and the name and extension number of the person in Accounting handling your account.

I put a transparent plastic pocket page at the beginning of each chapter so I can file things I don't have time to deal with or extra information pertaining to that particular account. I also have a chapter in the back of the three-ring binder comprised of "paid" bills.

By setting up your book this way you will have a continuing record of exactly what you have been billed, when it was billed, what and when payment was made. Mark on each bill the amount you paid, the date you paid it, and the check number. If insurance also paid on the bill, you will want to highlight that payment so you will know the exact balance due. Be sure to put any payment receipts into the plastic pocket page. After everything is said and done you will know what you are responsible for.

INSURANCE PAPERS AND STATEMENTS

In the front of my three-ring binder, I have a chapter for insurance papers. The insurance policy can go there. Payment claim forms that you need to fill out and send with bills not directly billed by the doctor can go there. Also, the statements you receive from the insurance company, listing what has and has not been paid, should be put into chronological order and kept into this chapter.

I use highlighter pens to track what is paid and how much. When I receive an insurance statement, I find the date of service. Then turn to my book, find the corresponding bill, and verify that the insurance company and I were billed the same amount. I highlight the bill amount, and I highlight the same amount on the insurance statement. If the amount paid by the insurance company does not cover the entire medical bill, I write on the medical bill what the balance is and the date of the insurance payment. You will then be able to look at each bill (without having to again look up an insurance statement) and know what your portion of the bill is.

Look at the back or bottom of the insurance statement to find out why the entire amount was not paid. Sometimes a deductible has not been met, and you will receive credit towards the deductible when you pay this bill. As soon as you meet your annual deductible, the insurance company will pay as listed in your policy. The "comments" section will normally tell you why they are not paying the entire amount. If you don't agree with them, you can call and dispute their findings.

When an insurance company receives a bill from your doctor, they will enter it into the computer for verification of insurance. Do you have coverage to cover this claim? After determining it is a covered claim, they will examine bill and make sure everything is correct. If it is a large bill, the insurance company may opt to pay a percentage of the bill "subject to audit." This means you are going to have only a portion of the bill paid initially. The decision to pay the balance is deferred until an audit of the entire bill can be performed. During the audit process, the insurance company will look at the bill closely and make sure everything that is billed is correct and in line with the treatment you received.

A few words of caution: *Audits can take a very long time.* Very often the insured does not even know it is happening. Sometimes you receive a bill and you just think the insurance has paid all they are going to pay; you start paying the balance. Of course, the hospital will take your money without telling you that this might be covered by your insurance because an audit is being performed. After the audit is completed, the insurance company will pay whatever they came up with that was fair and just. But the hospital will keep billing you for the unpaid balance. If the bill was not paid in full, the patient needs to ask: *Why was it not paid?* If the insurance company found an ineligible charge and refused to pay it, did the hospital take the charge off the bill or did they keep billing it?

In a case that I handled, a patient was billed for over $3,000 worth of medication that he had never received. It was "normal protocol" for these injections, so the hospital billed for them. We had the doctor's medical notes pulled and found documentation showing treatment was different for this patient—that the doctor had discontinued that specific course of treatment. It was a mistake that could have slipped through the cracks, and the patient would have had to pay an incorrect amount.

Look at your bills and question them. Look at the insurance statements and question them. Keep records and make sure everything fits together. If it doesn't, keep trying to find out why. Ask questions until you feel your questions have been answered.

FUND-RAISING CAMPAIGN

In chapter 8 we will discuss the building blocks of a successful fund-raising campaign. The family, and especially the patient, needs to be aware of what is happening on their behalf, but as I said earlier, they should distance themselves from the actual campaign and concentrate on getting well.

Get out the three-ring binder and put in a chapter for Fund-raising Help. In this chapter you will keep track of:

- what is happening and when;
- who is in charge of the event;
- things you need to do;
- names and phone numbers of those working on the event;
- any special notes pertaining to what is going on.

In this chapter you should list the names and phone numbers of media people who have contacted you. Your fund-raising committee should handle most of the information that the media people need, but asking the reporter for a business card will save time and energy, should you need to contact them. If reporters call you directly, you can forward them on to the event coordinator. We will discuss dealing with the media in chapter 9.

You will find it easier to keep control of your responsibilities if you have an event calendar for your records. You may not always feel like going to events, but if you do, it does help. Have your volunteers give you a calendar, and keep it in your book.

ORGANIZED CONTROL

Some families are comfortable allowing an "outsider" to help with financial matters; some find it very difficult. You need to determine and make clear who will do what. The BOX needs to be used. Bills need to be dealt with in a timely matter. Your three-ring binder needs to be utilized so it can make dealing with everything easier. If a little time is taken in setting up and organizing, a great deal of time will be saved later.

Many families have gotten through major medical problems only to face the incredible mess of trying to dig their way out financially. If you take the time to set things up correctly in the first place, you will not have to go back and reconstruct everything.

Whether you use a three-ring binder, a box, or a computer, you need to have a place to throw everything—a place to find something that is lost, a place to turn to for names and numbers. Whether you are sick, going in fifty directions at once, or just trying to figure out what to do next, a three-ring binder will bring everything together in one place.

FIVE

DEFINING YOUR NEEDS

In some ways it seems that we shouldn't even have to have this chapter. If you are sick and need help, you shouldn't have to explain why. *Medically related expenses* are those expenses resulting from the medical procedure or need for a treatment. When a patient goes to the public for money, everyone has the right to know what he or she are going to use the money for. I have worked with some families that thought they needed money but—after reviewing their income, health benefits, and those offered by the local medical school—discovered they were in better shape than they thought.

I can't repeat this enough: *Find out what you need, set a goal, and go after it.* Don't ask for more than you need. Document in writing where you feel the money (and state amounts) will be spent. Follow the outline I have here, and fill in the amounts:

Remember, many of these costs are tax deductible, so keep receipts and records of everything you spend.

1. Add up all current outstanding bills that have accumulated.
2. Ask the doctors, hospital, and care facilities what they envision as far as future care.
3. If the medical facility has a Social Services Department, ask its personnel about expected costs. They will no doubt pass you on to the Accounting Department, but you will have opened

the door to seeing what the hospital has to offer. Tell the SS worker you are investigating how much your bill will be, what will be covered, and how to pay the balance. For major medical costs, the hospital will verify your insurance before starting treatment and will be able to give you figures and payment options. Remember, they want their money; it is a lot easier for them to make prior arrangements than go after you when the procedure is done.

4. When you've contacted the accounting departments of all the places you will owe money, ask approximate costs, figure what insurance will pay, and then come up with a balance.

5. Determine what you can pay yourself.

6. Determine what "other" resources will pay. (We discussed "other" resources in chapter 2.)

7. List extra related costs.

   a. Travel costs (i.e., plane fares and/or gas) if medical facility is away from home.

   b. Prescriptions not covered by any other benefits.

   c. Lost wages for time off work.

   d. Compensation for family and/or friends to defray their cost for gas, food, and lodging as they take care of you away from home. At the transplant centers I have dealt with, the SS worker has a packet of information that walks you through what you will need and where to find it. When you are away from home for two to three months, the costs add up. Many facilities have home markets where you can borrow pots, pans, sheets, etc. The SS worker will give you a list of grocery stores nearby. ASK, ASK, ASK.

   Quick story: When our family had been in Seattle three months, we learned that we could get parking tokens to park in the hospital garage for free. We had been spending $65 a month for parking for three months. This doesn't even include parking meters for quick trips or relatives' parking fees.

e. Estimate ongoing and upcoming expenses that you won't be able to meet. This covers everything from property taxes, firewood, health insurance premiums, and everything in between. Some of these costs will raise questions about whether or not money raised from the public should go for these expenses, but the rule of thumb most groups use is:

If the income of the patient/parent has been reduced because of caring for a child or a patient has been unable to work (and there is verification of lost wages), some ongoing household expenses *may* be covered upon approval of the fund-raising committee or trustee.

8. If there is a donor involved, be sure to add in donor search costs. They add up fast.

9. Figure in pre- and posttreatment costs. After a major medical procedure, recovery can take much more time than the actual procedure. Maybe you will be able to only work part time for a year. What will it cost to get through that time?

10. What income will you have?

11. List any other medically related expenses directly caused by the patient's treatment or need for treatment.

As I have said before, the average family I surveyed that had gone through a bone marrow transplant had spent an average of $28,000 over and above what was covered. This money was out of their pockets. This was in 1994, so you can figure it is probably higher now.

When going to the public for funds, a patient can never be too careful about accounting for all funds raised. Most nonprofit fund-raising groups have the patient appoint a trustee, not a family member, to oversee how funds are spent. There have been many cases of families going to the public, raising a ton of money, and then spending it on cars, furniture, and things unrelated to medical care. When word spreads there is a need and television picks up on the story, a great deal of money can be raised in a short period of time. Great care is needed to protect the public interest. I always caution groups by saying, *"Not only are you raising money for this patient, but you are also raising it for the next one in need. Someone else will have to go to the community and ask for help in the future. If you, as a group or as a patient, misuse funds or lie, it will reflect on the next patient in need, and how successful they will ultimately be."*

At all times maintain a complete and accurate record of all funds raised and all funds spent. If during the campaign the news media or other group wants an accounting, be able to give it to them right away. Do not hesitate to state what the need is, how much has been raised, how much has been spent, and for what.

It is difficult to say exactly how much money you will be needing. You can come to a "best guess" figure by asking those who have gone through what you are facing. Many groups have figures that can help you. Call the American Cancer Society, the MDA, or organizations set up to assist people in fighting your medical problem. If you don't know where to start, ask you doctor if there are any organizations that can offer you help.

Come up with the best figure you can. It won't be carved in stone; it can be changed if it needs to be. Your volunteers need to know what kind of amount they are looking to raise. Remember, you need to know where you are going before you can know when you get there.

SIX

HELP!

AND WHERE TO FIND IT

Volunteers come from every corner of your world; they reach out to help when you need it. Some are close to you, some you have never met. You can raise money without helpers, but I will guarantee that you will be more successful if you have people willing to step out of their world into yours and help you do the things that need to be done to raise the funds you need. One person cannot do it all. A well-organized (and even a not so well-organized) group of loving, caring friends can enable you to reach your goals quicker and with less stress than if you try to do everything yourself. Besides, if you can reach twenty people willing to donate to you, just think how many people fifty friends could reach. You need to use every resource you have available to you. Let people know about your need, train them on the basics of your endeavors, and help them to keep motivated to reach your and their goals.

If given the opportunity to help, people you have never heard of will step forward and offer their time and expertise. Usually these people will be of great benefit to you. However, because these people can and do represent you in your cause, care must be taken to prevent a person you have never met from taking advantage of you and your efforts. A longtime friend who has worked in the fund-raising business for many years once told me that 30 percent of what is raised usually goes in the pocket of someone with access to the funds collected. thirty percent of $10,000 is $3,000. What can $3,000 do for you right now?

Well-intenioned people, saying they represent you and speak for you and your group, can fly off on their own and unintentionally hinder your efforts. Use everyone who volunteers, but make sure you or someone you can trust is overseeing the efforts.

Volunteers have lives of their own. A volunteer's time frame for help will vary. Volunteers usually have to get back to their lives within a ninety-day period. Knowing this, you can then plan your efforts around a three-month period. Not everyone will quit in ninety days, but understand that some will only be around for a short time. If you have to raise $300,000 in a ninety-day period, you better make sure every minute counts. (We'll talk about this in chapter 10.)

Usually at least one person in a group will not only see you through your campaign, but will also go on to help others. It might be through a national organization dedicated to helping people like yourself, or by starting a local organization to help patients and their families.

In finding people to help you, a very basic philosophy will work over anything else:

> *You need to have people believe in what you are trying to accomplish. You don't need to pay or give them anything if they truly believe in why you are trying to raise money.*

Family members usually offer solid support. If raising and/or donating funds will save their loved one's life, they will do it. They don't want to consider the alternative. But you also need to convince nonfamily members, even people you do not know, that your need is important enough for them to give up part of their busy schedule to help you. This belief theory also works when asking potential donors to give you money. If they *believe* in what you are doing and why you are doing it, they will give you a donation. If undecided, they will think about it; if they don't believe in your cause, they will pass you by. Belief is a very important key to unlocking the door to getting people to help you in all facets of finding help and money.

Many patients and their families are at a loss when beginning their journey into the new world of asking for help. Some are lucky enough that when the need is known, the volunteers step forward to help. Even when this happens, there are never too many. You can always use more people.

If you know why people are volunteering, you can place them in positions that can produce a high level of commitment. Their enthusiasm will help drive the group. Learn about their skills and background as well. Matching volunteers' needs with their abilities and giving them lots of thanks will keep them motivated. It's a win-win situation.

Quick story: A sweet little old lady came to the first meeting that was announced in the newspaper. No one knew her. She didn't say anything, just sat in the back of the room nodding her head. After the meeting was over and everyone was standing around visiting, someone went over and found out this woman's son had gone through exactly what the patient was facing. She thought she might be able to help in some small way. She was retired, her son and husband had both passed away, and she had time on her hands and prior bookkeeping experience. Knowing why she wanted to help and that she had the ability to be an asset to the group allowed the group to turn to her for guidance. She ended up handling all the funds that came in, all the reporting to the media on how the group was doing, and speaking to local organizations about how important it was for them to help the patient find the funds needed.

When working with volunteers:

- Give them a clear idea of what they need to do.
- Make sure they know what the goals are.
- Try to keep everything positive and uplifting.

- Be sure to give thanks and recognition whenever possible.

When structuring your volunteer group, keep in mind what kind of people fit in what kind of jobs. There are three kinds of volunteers.

- *Power people* can talk to anyone and are not afraid to step out of their comfort zone and "ask for the order."
- *Fulfillment people* can organize anything and work well with goals.
- *People people* make everything work. They are ever-present, always there when you need them—the worker bees.

In the following pages we will try to break down the different resources you have available to you for finding volunteers. By no means are these the only sources. They are a beginning point and can most certainly be expanded. Having said all this, I have to add that in *every* group I have worked with, people fall into whatever spot they are intended. You don't need to interview each and every one and place them into a position; people naturally gravitate to where they are most comfortable. Power people have a way of coming to the front and leading the group. Fulfillment people seem to just get down to business. People people just do what they are told. Make sure that a people person is not the one responsible for going before groups to state your cause. It won't get done, because that person often is uncomfortable speaking in front of crowds. Don't try to push square pegs into round holes. Each and every committee has a purpose, and they all need to be successful if you are to reach your goal.

FAMILY

Those closest to you are the easiest to recruit. They come forward, jump in, and do what needs to be done. They don't need convincing, pep talks or compensation. They are the group that will usually kick off a fund-raising campaign. We are going to discuss the family first, because they are the closest to you. They can be the greatest help, yet they can be the hardest to work with.

Family structure extends to all facets of our lives. Each family member relates to the family circle in a unique and different way. As we discussed earlier, each person has traits that place him or her in a position of comfort. If all goes well, each individual will bring to your campaign what it needs.

Grandparents seem to be the ones who bring wide contacts that are able to help. Grandma and Grandpa might not feel up to the everyday stress of making speeches or dealing with the media, but they can do a great letter writing project. One grandfather I knew was a doctor. He sent letters and a return envelope to everyone he knew or ever knew. He just stated the need, asked for help, and friends and colleagues responded with close to $10,000 in dona- tions. I met a grandmother who had a great group of ladies she had been playing golf and bridge with for twenty-five years. When they heard her granddaughter needed help, they organized a golf tour- nament and wrote a $4,000 check to the fund-raising campaign.

Parents have a vested interest in a patient. They have been through the good and the bad. They will do anything that needs to be done if it means there is a hope of saving their child. However, not only do parents play a very active role in the medical treatment and recovery process, but they also must handle all the ongoing day- to-day chores a family faces when someone is seriously ill. Parents will do what needs to be done, but if a volunteer group is develop- ing, my advice is to leave the parents to help with the treatment and recovery side of this great adventure.

Siblings, depending upon their age, can go in many different directions. They are there to help the patient, but, because the patient takes so much family attention, they also are sometimes on the outer edge. Brothers and sisters of all ages, given the opportunity, will come up with some innovative ideas on how to raise money. They know the family's circle of friends and interests and are able to recruit very effectively for the patient. One brother lived one thousand miles from where his sister lived, but still in the town where his family grew up. He went to the school where his sister graduated from and got a list of her classmates. Not only did he start a letter writing campaign, but at *his* class reunion he talked his classmates into organizing and hosting a community circus benefiting his sister. His classmates got to see each other while accomplishing something great for someone else.

Another little sister was feeling rather left out of everything. She went to her teacher and asked if there was something her class could do to help. The teacher went to the principal and talked to the patient's former teachers. The school organized a fun day at the school, with the students running all the events. Parents were invited and encouraged to play "children" games. Of course, they had to pay an entry fee, but were rewarded with handmade prizes from each of the classes. Imagine the pride of contribution when little sister, age nine, presented her school's check for $700 to the fundraising committee.

No matter how young or old, each person wants to be involved in some way. It may be giving advice, writing a check, or running the whole show, but don't leave anyone out. You need everyone.

Having brought up the good stories, I need to put in a word of caution. Families feel a sense of ownership to a patient, as it should be. However, sometimes a family member will overstep his/her importance. More than once, I have seen a family member meet with the press and discuss issues about the patient they had no right to discuss. Or a well-meaning family member might open a bank account and start telling people to deposit their donations into this account before everything is organized.

I knew one patient who had four different accounts in four different banks set up for her, before anyone really knew what needed to be raised or where the funds would go. Trying to bring everything together *after* it is in a total mess wastes valuable time. In such a situation, each person who set up an account thinks that account should be the one kept and all the rest should be combined and deposited into it. Depending upon how the accounts were set up and in what name, *all* the accounts could be incorrect. I have discussed earlier that it is important to NOT have a bank account in the patient's name because the patient may (otherwise) be able to qualify for state or federal funds such as Medicaid or Social Security.

When a volunteer group is formed, each helper needs to understand how the patient and the immediate family wants to handle the tasks at hand. Whether it is a family member, a friend, or a person off the street, each needs to work within the guidelines of the group, within the established time frame and structure. If someone has an idea, they should bring it up to the group in a meeting and discuss if and how it can be brought in to the campaign. This rule is for family and volunteers.

FRIENDS

If you are fortunate enough to have friends close by willing to pitch in and help, please do not hesitate to ask. Friends can be your greatest asset. First of all, they don't have to deal with the day-to-day chores that go along with caring for a patient. Second, they can bring a whole different source of ideas and volunteers into the situation. Third, they might know someone you don't, who knows someone that can open a door through which you would never have thought you could get help.

Friends are removed enough that they can serve as trustees and "keepers" of the funds, preventing anyone having even remote grounds to suspect or say the family misspent funds. Friends are close enough to be able to ask how things are really going, but won't tell the entire community. They will be able to go to the volunteer group and share the need for completing fund-raising projects quickly.

Friends can go to the community and ask on behalf of the patient. No one likes to get up and say *they* need help. A friend can do that for you.

When looking for friends, look in every corner. Start with your closest and end with those you haven't seen in twenty years. A phone call can open up doors to so many different avenues. You can't afford not to ask.

SPHERE OF INFLUENCE

A salesman's success often depends on what the sales industry calls a "sphere of influence." Large companies spend large of amounts of money to train sales staff on how to develop a large sphere. Your sphere of influence is all the people around that touch your life. When I was in sales, I was taught to think of my life as a big circle. You are in the center, and everyone else who touches your life is in this circle. You start from the center and work out. Your sphere consists of:

You	Your family	Your friends
Church members	Your married children's in-laws	Club members
Your lawyer	Children's friends' parents	Neighbors
Teachers (current & former)	Your dentist	Coworkers
Your veterinarian	Your doctor	Bank tellers
Fellow classmates	Your banker	Waitress
Grocery store clerk	Exercise partners	Baby-sitter

These are just a few of the people who touch your life. Everyone from the closest family member to your newspaper boy or mail carrier is in your sphere. Don't be afraid to ask them for help. The goal is to get as many people working on your goals, so you reach as many people as you can.

Within this sphere certain *groups* can be brought to the fore-front. They should be developed for who they are and what they do. Church, little league, neighborhood groups, PTA, and 4-H all have inner structures that your volunteer base can key into to help broaden your group. These groups are used to raising money for various causes, including their own. If a fellow member or a member's child or relative needs help, they will tap into their own resources and develop a plan of action their particular group can implement. Your group just needs to supply them with information about the needs and goals of your efforts. Give them an overview of why you are raising money, where it is going, and how much you need.

CHURCHES

Most churches have a very strong inner circle. The members are used to working together. They do many things in their everyday lives that include each other. Raising money keeps their church going. It doesn't matter what religion you are; the basic principles are the same. We are put on this earth to help our fellow man. How your particular church goes about raising money or offering help is up to them.

As I mentioned earlier, one church formed a plan to open a home to a patient's family members having to live one thousand miles from home for three months. The family had a warm loving "family" to come home to after a day at the hospital. Another church offered its facilities for numerous events to be held in its recreation center. Still another had a community potluck and charged for the meal, raising close to a $1,000 dollars.

Every church day, prayer groups are praying for the healing of a fellow church member. Congregations come together to fill the needs of people needing help. Again, you have to let them know what your needs are. Even if it seems remote that they will be able to help, you just won't know until you ask.

Church youth groups are fun to work with. They come up with such great ideas. They not only come up with a plan, but they volunteer their time to carry it out. Let people know your need and see what can happen.

Because church members are so used to working together, if your group can get a church to work with you, your group has grown by the number of people in that church. A subcommittee can be formed to work with the church membership.

SCHOOLS

I had the great pleasure of working with a teacher who needed a bone marrow transplant. It was close to the beginning of my "education" in fundraising. To this day I marvel at how everyone helped Bob out. An entire town came to his aid. Not only did they help him, but they also raised money to do marrow donor testing so the National Marrow Donor Registry could grow. I could write a separate book on all the things that happened in that town. Every element that I have written about here was utilized in one way or another.

Bob was and is a teacher. His sphere of influence reached many different people. He was active in his church and community. His fellow teachers rallied behind him. His church opened its doors. The community not only donated money to his cause, but the citizens had their blood tested and were added to the National Registry. There were community meetings of volunteers. Special church services were devoted to Bob's special needs. Civic organizations came forth and helped with fund-raisers. Students had pizza pickup and delivery sales with a portion of the pizza price being donated to

Bob's cause. The media had special articles about Bob and what he was going through—what it meant to be a marrow donor. They gave updates on fund-raising and when and where events were being held.

Through all of this, Bob's fellow teachers handled the massive amount of work required to pull this off. Everyone in the community was aware of what needed to be done, how it was being done, and when it got done. To this day I marvel at how everyone came out and helped in so many different ways. This is just one of many stories I could tell about how a town turned out to attain an unreachable goal.

Try to get a member from each school in the community to help your group. Whether they work together or work only with their own school, they should be encouraged to find their own separate fund-raiser. Make sure each representative has all the information about what is needed and why. Give them the space to come up with whatever their school wants to do.

SERVICE CLUBS AND ORGANIZATIONS

Whether you call them service clubs, lodges, or fraternal organizations, they are all groups of people who come together to serve others, each with their own purpose and a charter that states why they are there. They are used to fund-raising. They also have fun helping out in other directions too. As I mentioned earlier, one group got together and cut and stacked a firewood supply for a patient needing a transplant. Another group volunteered its entire membership to help put on a rodeo and pancake feed for a patient. They took care of everything from the parking to garbage hauling. Did they give money? Nope, but their efforts sure were worth a bundle.

Every Chamber of Commerce has a list of organizations in its community. Sometimes the Chamber will charge a small fee to get this list, but it is well worth the money. Once you have the list, follow this basic outline:

- Compile a letter and mail to each group telling of your needs.
- Ask to come to their meeting and tell the membership about your campaign.
- Give them a list of needs and a time frame.
- Ask them to help, and ask them to let you know what they can do.
- Give them a time you need to know by.
- Send them a thank-you note regardless of whether they help or not.

Try to get a member from each organization to join your group. Let them do their own thing, but have them keep you informed on what is happening within their group. Keep in mind that groups have speakers lined up well in advance for their meetings. Sometimes it is not possible to speak before a group. Don't give up; find out how your goals can be theirs. Ask if they will just write out a check. Be flexible and see what the group can come up with.

OCCUPATIONAL RESOURCES

We have already discussed fellow employees and how they can help. Even if you work in a small office, there are people you come into contact daily who can offer help. The bigger the office doesn't mean the bigger the help. Again, let your needs be known and see what can happen.

Unions offer a unique opportunity. First, they have a wide mailing list. Depending upon your company's structure, you might be able to send out a plea via e-mail. One group I worked with was raising money for the small son of a U.S. Forest Service employee. E-mail got the word out, and the U.S. postal system brought the donations in—enough money to help another employee who needed medical funds but didn't know to ask for help until seeing the e-mail appeal.

Whatever means your profession uses to disseminate news to its members — newsletters, bulletin boards, conventions—try to lock in on that method. Don't rule out anything. I even saw a town send out letters requesting help in the electric bills sent to each home-owner. Whatever works is what you should do.

When going to "The BIG Boys," or national corporations, I have found the hardest task is to find out whom to ask. If you know people in the corporation, ask them with whom they would start. No doubt you will have to go through a number of people, but ask where to *start*. If you call on the phone, be prepared to be transferred a num-ber of times. Just keep asking for the person who handles company donations and community projects. Try to stay in your own town when asking a business to help. There are many opportunities close by. Companies such as Wal-Mart are very active in their communi-ties. Ask them for help.

You need to know as much as you can about the business. When you find the right person, ask if the company has "giving" guidelines. Follow those guidelines to the letter.

Remember, companies get lots of requests for help. Personalize your letter. Never send a form letter! Craft an appeal that will touch whoever reads it. If they ask for a one-page letter stating what the need is, give them a one-page letter. State how this donation will help the business and/or its employees. Give the business time to make a decision. No matter what happens, *always* send a letter thanking them for talking with you. If they give to your group, keep them informed on your progress and where their money went.

The following outline is one I used whenever I was going into a business. It works most of the time because it offers choices.

CORPORATE SPONSORS

Informing Employees about the Problem

1. Have a volunteer come and talk to their employees.
2. Hand out a flier about the goals of your groups.
3. Allow written materials to be distributed in paycheck envelopes.

Helping: Provide Materials to Employees Explaining:

1. how can they help.
2. when they can help.
3. where they should go.

Contributions

1. Money
2. Time
3. Merchandise

Advertising

1. Allow the group to use the business name as a supporter.
2. Tell about your needs in any company publications.
3. Include in company advertising a short appeal for help with your project.

Support

1. Solicit their ideas on raising money.
2. Solicit advertising ideas.
3. Ask if someone in their organization can help your group.
4. Ask if there are other people or companies your group should contact.

FOLLOW UP

Businesses always want to know where their money went. On what was it spent?

ALWAYS thank them. ALWAYS let them know how the group did. ALWAYS thank them again. Creative ways of thanking businesses are a great way to ensure the next time someone needs help, that company will offer support.

SEVEN

ORGANIZATIONS AND

FOUNDATIONS

When you go to the public and ask for money, decide whether to conduct a fund-raising campaign on your own, or turn to a fund-raising organization. There are professional fund-raising organizations as well as nonprofit organizations. In this chapter we will discuss the difference between for-profit and not-for-profit groups, the pros and cons of using each, and what they can do for you. There are all kinds of different organizations, each with it's own set of rules.

Do you need to use an outside group? For some things you face, I would say it is much easier to have a group come in and take over. Whether for profit or not, most organizations handle a fund-raising campaign basically the same way. A for-profit organization will charge you a percentage of everything that is raised, a not-for-profit organization will not. Each should have a clear cut set of guidelines to inform you of exactly what they will do, what will happen to the money you raise, and how much, if anything, it will cost you.

Read these guidelines and ask questions. Ask for references. Talk to families that have worked with the group you are considering. Check with your state Attorney General's Office, and make sure there aren't any problems with the group. Ask to see its Internal Revenue Employer Identification Number. What is its "Foundation Status Classification" with the federal government? You have a right to ask for a copy of their tax statements from the previous year.

You need to be very careful about whom you align yourself with. We all have heard stories and read about people who have gone to the public, raised money and misspent it. Check out the organization by talking to the executive director, not just the person in charge of campaigns. Get documentation showing that the group is legitimate. Read all materials carefully before signing any agreements. Make sure you understand what you are signing on for.

USING AN OUTSIDE ORGANIZATION

In a nutshell, most organizations will help you by:

- Organizing fund-raising campaigns and volunteers
- Working directly with the media and preparing media releases
- Offering hints and suggestions
- Helping solve problems through contacts they already have established
- Overseeing the distribution of funds and the setting up of bank accounts
- Educating you, your volunteers, and your community to the problems you are facing
- Offering the use of their nonprofit status (discussed chapter 2 and chapter 8) for tax-deductible donations
- Offering their established name and reputation as a way of legitimizing your group's efforts.
- Offering to help others with excess money raised, beyond what is needed by the patient.
- Providing access to varied large corporate sources for help for specific needs (i.e., airlines that help with travel costs).

Most groups are formed because the people behind the group have walked the walk you are now walking. They have been there and know what you are facing. They know firsthand the problems you are having, and they have found ways to solve them. It is the old adage, "Why reinvent the wheel?" Because they know what happens out there, they are better able to guide you through the twists and turns. They have experience in forming fund-raising volunteer groups. They know what works and what doesn't. Experience counts when you are racing against time.

With a full-time staff, the group is better able to promote your cause and make sure everything is carried out. They have guidelines for the volunteers to follow, so no one has to figure out what to do.

Most organizations will come to your town and put on a campaign organizational meeting for the volunteers you have enlisted. They will outline what your needs are, how the campaign will go, and ask for volunteers to head different committees. The leadership will follow specific protocols on how to raise the money, where it will be deposited, and how it will be spent.

Before the organization does anything, it will have you sign an agreement specifically stating what everyone is going to do. The group might ask you to send a letter from the doctor documenting that the person is indeed sick and needs help. It is not unusual for the group to ask for bank account statements to verify the need. You need to understand this group has a reputation and, as an organization registered with the IRS, needs to make sure what it does falls within the guidelines set forth by the IRS. It is subject to audit and can be fined or closed down if it breaks any laws.

In most cases the organization establishes a local bank account. All funds raised are deposited in this account. The funds are then transferred into the organization's corporate bank account. The amount raised is set aside to be used by the designated individual. When bills start coming in, a local volunteer will review and pass them on to the organization for payment. We will discuss this further in chapter 8.

Some patients and families have a problem with not having access to the bank funds. I explain to them this is protection for the community, the patient, and the family. By having the organization handle the money, there is never any question about how it was spent. No one can come back later and say you bought a new car with money that was supposed to go to medical bills.

In most cases, organizations are registered as nonprofit groups; people will give bigger donations because they are tax deductible. Many businesses will not donate to an individual, but will give to an organization that is designating specific funds for a patient because they can use the money they donate for a tax deduction.

Professional fund-raising groups run their operations the same way as nonprofits; the only difference seems to be that they charge a fee. Percentages vary from organization to organization. Nonprofits seem to be busier, but the differences are minimal.

Pay close attention to every detail when dealing with people or businesses you don't know. If you deal with telemarketing busi-nesses, be sure you know how the money will be divided before you sign up with them. There is nothing sadder than signing on with a tele-fundraiser, having their representatives solicit funds for you, or sell tickets to an event, only to have them keep 50 to 75 percent of everything raised or sold.

Quick story: A very active group raising money for a young father had been doing everything it could—from holding garage sales to penny drives. A for-profit telemarketer business contacted the group and offered to sell tickets for a concert to be held at the community ballpark. The volunteer group agreed to handle every-thing at the ball field—the entertainment, parking, and rental of the field. The group budgeted everything out and figured how many tickets needed to be sold. Because so many had jumped in to vol-unteer their time and efforts, they were very surprised when the tele-marketer gave them only a fraction of what was raised. It had kept its "cut" off the top. The volunteer group got stuck paying for every-thing and losing money on the concert.

CHARITABLE FOUNDATIONS

As we have discussed, many groups and organizations offer help for specific diseases. Some have lists of fund-raising groups they have used in the past. Contact your local or state chapter and get information from them. They are an excellent source for determining and evaluating a particular group's benefits.

Even if the group can't offer help to an individual because they are there for the general public, it can give valuable help by sharing resources they have used in the past. They can work closely with professional fund-raising groups to form a coalition with the best contacts available.

EIGHT

LET'S RAISE MONEY

This chapter contains information already discussed for a reason. If you have volunteers or friends helping you to raise money, they can take this one chapter and have the basic outline to put on a successful campaign. No one will utilize this "entire" book, but one chapter is quick and easy to absorb.

GOALS AND NEEDS

DETERMINE BASIC AMOUNTS NEEDED

In every campaign it is vitally important to know what you will be asking the public to give you . Have the family determine its needs. Basic questions that can be asked are (chapter 5):

1. Do you have any idea as to the immediate costs now accumulating?
2. What kind of medical insurance coverage do you have? How much does it cover and for what? Have you received pre-authorization from the insurance company for major treatments (chapter 3)?
3. What are the projected long-term costs? If you haven't any idea, you must sit down with the doctor and ask very pointed questions.

4. Is there any outside help available (chapter 2)?

5. What are your current assets (i.e., checking and savings accounts, etc.)?

6. Do you have a budget for your current monthly expenses with income and expenditures? List all your current outstanding bills, what you pay each month, and the current balance. Next, write down what extra costs will be incurred because of the illness/treatment (chapter 5). In other words, come up with a figure.

TIME FRAMES

When assessing time frames, you need to examine the family needs and determine if there is time to spare in coming up with funds. If a patient needs $1,500 in a week to enter a hospital for treatment, then you need to look at events that will take place quickly.

Volunteers have a work span time of generally 90 to 120 days. Fund-raising is a time consuming affair, and to be successful you need to devote intensive, countless hours to preparing and then carrying out your events. Most everyone wants to help, but a person can only stop his/her life for so long to devote the time needed for this kind of volunteerism.

If your goal is to raise $300,000 and you know volunteers will start going back to their lives in 120 days, then it's easy to figure out your group has to raise approximately $75,000 each month. This will help determine what kind of events need to be held. If bake sales only raise approximately $300, you will have to make lots of cakes to make your $75,000 per month goal. (See chapter 10 for event ideas.)

After the volunteer committee has come up with a list of events, look at each one and determine how long will it realistically take to get the event off the ground. When will the event take place? Tentatively mark it on a calendar; it can always be changed later.

Determine a realistic figure for how much you think the event will raise. Be sure to figure in how much it will cost to carry out the event. Hopefully, everything will be donated, but usually there are some costs to everything you do. (See chapter 10 for approximate costs on some events.)

When looking at the entire picture of how to raise funds, be sure not to overlook things that can be taking place while your group is concentrating on major fund-raising events. Canisters and envelopes being sent out will bring in money with little continuing effort while you are busy organizing your events.

ACCOUNTABILITY AND CREDIBILITY

When going to the public and asking for money, a group needs to be very credible. I counsel people to be very careful in what they are doing, because some time down the road there will be someone else that will need this community's help. Plainly speaking, if your group makes a mess of things, the community will always remember.

DONATIONS: ARE THEY DEDUCTIBLE?

Half of all donations are given around the Christmas season, and only one-third of the donors know where their funds are actually going. Why should you know this? When figuring your plan of action, if it is around Christmas there are some real pros and cons. The pros: People are already programmed to give and want to help at this time of year. The con: You are going to be competing with the big charities that have their major fund-raising campaigns at that time.

Forewarned is forearmed, and there are things you can do to take advantage of this busy gift-giving time. Before we go into those fund-raising ideas, let's discuss some rules about donations—specifically, what is tax deductible and what isn't. Your group can advertise, "All donations tax deductible," but are they? People can only claim their donations if they itemize their expenses for tax purposes. About 50 percent actually itemize; the rest really don't have any tax advantages. For the big donors, however, it is a necessity to go through a nonprofit organization. We talked about this in chapter 7.

There are some simple rules to follow when asking for large donations. When preparing your fliers, tickets, and printed materials, state on the material, *"All donations tax deductible to the extent of the law. Please consult with your accountant."* This might seem a bit extreme, but it eliminates the burden of your group having to verify what is and what isn't deductible, how much is and how much isn't allowed. Many groups will step out and think because it is a donation, it is tax deductible. They tell everyone it is, not knowing otherwise. The problem arises when someone makes a donation, thinking it is deductible because your group told them it was, tries to claim it, and can't. This has happened, and it is not easy or cheap to straighten out. Be careful if you are asking for large donations.

We've discussed how to set things up correctly; now we'll address tax benefits and how to handle them. If someone gives you a check for $250 or more, you need to give a receipt. A cancelled check will no longer work for tax purposes. Donations over $500 need the donor to fill out a special tax form (Number 8283). This isn't your problem, but make sure you give all large donations proof of giving so they can have it for their records. If the donation is over $5,000 the nonprofit group, along with an appraiser, will have to fill out a part on the 8283 form verifying the value of the gift. So just because your fund-raising campaign lasted only a couple of months doesn't mean you can just close the books and be done. In most cases you can, but how successful you were in getting large donations determines how much liability there will be at tax time. Again, the best way to make sure you are covered is to keep good records, give receipts for all donations over $250, and make sure you are aligned with an IRS-recognized nonprofit organization in the first place.

What can people claim on their taxes? Of course they can claim straight donations of cash, but there are some other things that you might not be aware of. **VOLUNTEER EXPENSES**…yes, you can claim the costs to you to volunteer for a nonprofit organization. Mileage is a great example. Again, keep records of costs and ask your accountant. **BENEFIT TICKETS**…in most cases you can not claim the entire amount. The ticket should state the cost of the dinner. Deduct that from the ticket purchase price and the balance can be deducted. Your group should know this, and I will discuss it when we are going through what ideas work for fund-raising. Just know the only way the total benefit ticket is deductible is if there are no costs associated with the benefit.

Some things that *cannot* be deducted:

1. Raffle tickets (which we will discuss later)
2. Volunteer time. You cannot say you took off work for a day and turn your lost wages in as a donation.
3. Direct gifts to the needy. The only way a donation is tax deductible is if it goes through a recognized nonprofit organization. We have talked about this before, and we will again.

A "tax deductible" statement can bring in larger donations; just make sure that it is.

TWO QUESTIONS TO ALWAYS ASK WHEN MAKING A DONATION

1. What percentage is going to the program (patient)?
   In all gift giving everyone should know where the funds are going. We talked earlier about stating what your needs are. Your group needs to be ready with a percentage of how much

money will actually go to the patient's costs. Because we try to get everything donated, the goal should be 100 percents. This is not always possible. Some organizations take a percentage to help raise the money; sometimes there are direct costs in putting on a project. The easiest way to deal with this is to say you are not sure, but at the moment everything is being donated for this project, and no one is being paid to help raise the money. If you are going through a professional fund-raising group, they will deal with this issue themselves.

2. What is the mission statement of the group?

Before a dollar changes hands, the donor should be aware of what the group is trying to accomplish. For large organizations, a mission statement will lay out in twenty-five words or less what their group's mission is. Your group might not be an American Red Cross or a United Way, but everyone out raising money in your group should be able to tell anyone asking exactly what you as a group are trying to accomplish. Making this mission statement short and concise makes it much easier to get your goals across.

I am bringing up these questions because if you know what donors ask before giving any donations, then you will know the answers to give them when asking for money.

501C3 ORGANIZATIONS

Try to team up with a 501c3 organization. (See chapter 7.) An organization with an IRS nonprofit designation (501c3) can help raise money for causes and all the donations will be tax deductible to the donor. This is important because people will give more if they know they can get a tax deduction. Many businesses will not consider donating money, let alone large ticket items such as cars, if you do not work through a nonprofit organization. Service organizations, churches, and many volunteer children and civil organizations such as the volunteer firemen in your community can help lend their designation. Be sure you do not ask them to violate their own particular bylaws in assisting your group.

The 501c3 group will allow you to have donations come to their organization in their name with a special designation for little Johnny. All checks must be made out to the 501c3 organization; they become the property of that organization. They can do anything they want with the money. Ask them to set up a special account for Johnny. Explain that your group will appoint a trustee to approve all bills that need to be paid before they are given to the 501c3 group for them to write out the checks. What you will be asking them to do is to help you:

- organize and raise money;
- deposit funds in their bank account;
- administer those funds when bills need paying;
- serve as the community's watchdog, and make sure the funds are going to where they were intended.

The family must know these funds are the property of the organization, not them. Families must realize getting a community to give them thousands of dollars requires a major step in establishing trust. By using a nonprofit organization it accomplishes two very important objectives:

1. It protects the donor by assuring him/her the funds are going to where they are designated and being used for medically related expenses.
2. It protects the family from anyone ever coming back and saying the funds were used for things other than for what they were intended.

TRUSTEE

In the administering of the funds it makes the process much easier if there is one person—approved by the patient and family and not a family member—to take control of working closely with the family and the group paying the bills in approving medically related expenses to be paid. This person needs to know what the fund-raising committee considers a medically related bill to be. The trustee's main job is to represent the interests of the community that has donated funds for medically related expenses. In most professional fund-raising groups, medically related expenses are defined as in the IRS publication "Medical and Dental Expenses." You may request a copy of this through the Department of the Treasury Internal Revenue Service, "Forms Distribution Center" for your state. Here are the addresses, depending on your state :

AK, AZ, CA, CO, HI, ID, MT, NV, NM, OR, UT, WY:
Forms Distribution Center
Western Area District Cent.
Ranch Cordova, CA 95743-0001

AL, AR, IL, IN, IA, KS, KY, LA, MI, MN, MS, MO, NE, ND, OH, OK, SD, TN, TX, WA:
Forms Distribution Center
Central Area District Cent.
P.O. Box 9903
Bloomington, IL 61799

CT, DE, DC, FL, GA, ME, MD, MA, NH, NJ, NY, NC, PA, RI, SC, VT, VA, WV:
Forms Distribution Center
Eastern Area District Cent.
P.O. Box 85074
Richmond, VA 23261-5074

ANY REMAINING MONEY

A question most often asked is: "What happens if we raise more money than we need?" A recognized fund-raising organization will include a clause in its contract stating what will be done with "remaining funds." Some will hold them indefinitely for the patient; some will hold them until a doctor's release is obtained and the patient is "cured." If the patient dies, all expenses should be paid before "remaining funds" can be established. Keep in mind this process takes a period of time to complete. As the surviving family, you want to make sure **ALL** bills have come in and are accounted for. After any and/or all things have happened then, in most cases, the funds revert to the organization to be used for another patient. It is best to ask direct questions of the organization and get answers that are backed up by the contract you signed as to how that particular organization deals with any remaining funds.

For those of you conducting the fund-raising campaign, it is very important you know how these funds are going to be used. Make sure your volunteers also know. When they are asked the inevitable question, they will be able to answer confidently. Where remaining funds are going to go needs to be answered before you start raising money. Some suggestions are:

- If a church or a service organization is involved, donate the money to them. They can keep it in an emergency fund for the next time someone comes to them for help. You would be surprised at how many times this can happen.
- If the fund-raising is for a patient with a specific disease, the money can be donated to a national organization that helps patients with that disease.
- Many times the family will have a specific hospital, clinic, or transplant center that could use the money. In one case I worked on, the family split the money between the transplant

center (which used the money to buy new pajamas for the kids), the home health group that helped take care of the baby, and the fund-raising organization that had given them guidance during their fund-raising endeavors.

One of the hardest things for a family and patient to do is to ask for help. The second hardest thing is to accept it. Stating that any unused money remaining after the campaign will go to help someone else really helps handle a stressful situation. I suggest saying to anyone offering money, "Yes, I need your help. But if we can raise more money than what I need, all the unused funds will go to help someone else not as lucky as I am to have the many helpful friends that I have."

BANK ACCOUNTS

Often the first thing that gets done in fund-raising is going to the local bank and setting up an account so people can make deposits. This is not always a wise thing to do, for a number of reasons. The first and foremost is, there is no control over the funds—either in the way of thanking people for donating or in how the money will be spent. I will say this a number of times throughout this book, "Be sure you set up everything, so when you are done with your fund-raising endeavors those coming after you will not have a problem with how YOU handled the money you raised."

Another problem can arise when the family or patient is receiving some kind of state or federal help. If they are receiving Medicaid or some other kind of assistance, the funds that are put into the account at the bank in their name can be counted as ordinary income and can therefore jeopardize any benefits they are entitled to because they have too much money to qualify. Also, they may very well be required to pay income taxes on some amounts. Many things need to be considered.

A common problem arises when there is more than one account set up, usually at different banks. When trying to go to the community and project a unified effort, it is very difficult if too many people are going in too many different directions. The media plays a very important role in community fund-raising (chapter 9). If there isn't any cohesiveness to the effort and too many things are happening with no real knowledge of how much has been raised and how it happened, you will lose credibility with both the people trying to support and report on the effort, and (most importantly) those thinking about making a donation.

Lastly, when everything does start to come together and there is a unified effort with a goal, plan and direction to go, all in place, it is very difficult to go back and try to change anything that was in place prior to what was set up by the family, patient, and fund-raising committee.

I know of an instance where a very dedicated group did everything by the book, had everything set up through an organized fund-raising organization. Then some people decided they were going to "help" but did not take the time to find out what was going on already and where funds were supposed to be deposited. They not only set up a bank account, but they also did something wrong and jeopardized the entire campaign's credibility with the community. They decided to hold a raffle and sell tickets. They raised $5,000. Some of the money was spent for prizes, some for dinner for the "helpers," and the rest was given to the patient via a check. Right off someone found out $500 was spent for "dinner." The organized group had been saying in all the press releases, "All funds will go for medically related expenses." So the "helpers" made a liar out of the group. Next, the state Justice Department contacted the organizer of the organized group (his/her name was in the paper as the contact person) and asked to verify the raffle license number used for the raffle, and there was none. (Yes, in most states it is against the law to hold raffles without a raffle license.) Of course that hit the news-papers too. To top it all off, the Social Service Department contacted the patient, verified the funds raised, and this amount was added into the patient's income. The patient no longer qualified for aid, having too much income. All for the best reasons, a great opportunity to help someone turned against an entire campaign. Keep control of all activities, funds, and how they are spent.

WHO WILL PAY THE BILLS?

The person paying the bills will work with the trustee to make sure all bills are correct, eligible, and paid in a timely matter. If you are dealing with an organized fund-raising group, the trustee just needs to go through the bills given to him/her by the patient or family, verify they meet the criteria for medically related expenses, and pass them on to the organized fund-raising group the patient has a contract with. The bills will then be reviewed by the group and paid. If there is a question, the group will contact the trustee to work out any problems or questions.

If you do not have a contract with an organized group, your fund-raising volunteers need to appoint someone to review and pay the bills. This person might be the treasurer of the fund-raising campaign. It is best not to have a family member do this job. The trustee will go ahead and collect and verify the bills and then pass them on for payment. There should be two signatures required on any check.

If you are using a service organization or church, the bills should be handled the same as if you were using an organized fund-raising organization.

Many times expenses arise that no one knows how to deal with. A vote of the group is always best in these circumstances. Case in point: The patient has to drive back and forth 150 miles for check-ups. His car develops a mechanical problem that costs $100 to fix. Should you pay it? Well, first ask if the problem can be fixed by explaining the situation to a mechanic and asking him to donate his time to fixing the problem instead of giving a donation to the fund-raising campaign. If that doesn't work, then ask if there is another way to get the patient to the appointment. If there isn't a cheaper way, then by all means pay the bill! Be careful! Case in point: Patient is a young boy; Mom and Dad are driving back and forth to the appointments; the engine blows up in their '69 Ford. They requested that the car engine be replaced or the group pay for a new car. It was cheaper to buy the mother and boy bus tickets for the last three appointments.

The best way to handle questionable expenses is to use common sense. Ask yourselves if there is anyway else you can deal with this. Try to work it out and keep the funds raised for medical needs for just that. A good rule of thumb is to ask, "If I pay this and it goes into the newspaper that I paid it, what will the donors say?"

MAILING ADDRESS AND CONTACT PHONE NUMBERS

A mailing address is needed for many reasons. First and foremost, donors might want to mail their donations. Also, if your group has a mailing campaign, you will need a return address and where to send donations. In the organizational meeting a mailing address should be established and then used throughout the campaign by everyone. Using one of the "new" mailing outlet shops that have popped up, such as Mail Express, has proven successful. When you approach them, you should have specific needs in mind: a specific time period and size of box. Ask them to donate it to the group. It never *hurts* to ask!

Contact phone numbers are used in many different ways and should be on all printed material, canisters, and anything about which there might be a question. The person the number belongs to needs to be a very understanding, dedicated volunteer. He/she will get phone calls at all times of the day and night. Many will be from people wanting to volunteer, give donations of materials or services, not to mention those who are already volunteering and are in a bind. A very successful campaign I know of got a voice mail company to donate a mobile phone and voice mail services to the group. The campaign coordinator was the phone person and handled all the calls. This cut down on a lot of confusion and got questions answered right away.

Both the contact phone number and address should be listed on all written materials. It should also be given out in every news media report. Again, your group wants to come off as very organized with a direction and a plan to get there. These are tools that make the job easier.

VOLUNTEER COMMITTEES AND KEY PEOPLE

Your key people are the ones heading the campaign efforts: the chairman (campaign coordinator), trustee, secretary/treasurer, and media and news liaison. Because of the time it takes to bring everything together, they should be people with both experience (working with groups and handling money) and the time to devote to this entire campaign. They should not be expected to have to work with each and every event, speech, or committee that takes place. They should be available to step in wherever needed and encouraged to keep things going.

CAMPAIGN COORDINATOR: Should be available throughout the entire campaign to help when needed. He or she needs to be able to work with people and communicate the needs of the group. The ability to get people involved and delegate is needed. Commitment is the key to this position. This person will be called upon to be on the firing line all the time. Usuall, a person will come to the front naturally. He/she will need to help recruit volunteers to fill committees. The coordinator will call and head meetings when needed and make sure all donors are thanked. Acknowledging the help of volunteers and keeping them motivated can help keep the group together until the goals have been met.

TRUSTEE: The family must pick this person carefully. This person works with the group to carry out the job of getting everything paid for. This job will no doubt last longer than the fund-raising campaign itself. Scrutinizing all bills and receipts that need to be submitted for payment can take a bit of time. If the trustee is willing to work within the volunteer group, it helps for him/her to know the wishes of not only the family of the patient, but the group itself.

SECRETARY/TREASURER: This person needs to be available because, in most cases, this individual has all the compiled information. Names, dates, times, amounts, goals—you name it—are his/her responsibility. When the media person needs to contact a reporter about the outcome of a particular event, this person needs to be there to answer the questions.

MEDIA AND NEWS LIAISON: This is a tricky position. Because the media can make or break a campaign, this person needs to have some understanding of how the media works. If you can find someone from the media world, this would be best. Only ONE person should work with the media and should be able to set up times and places for key players to be interviewed, be able to be reached at all times, and have answers to questions that arise. This person should be able to recruit the aid of printing companies to help with printed materials. Look for free advertising opportunities throughout the community. In other words, this person's job is to get the correct word(s) out, to tell anyone that asks how much money has been raised to date, how the patient is doing, when and where the next planned event is, etc.

All other committees will come to the surface as needed. There should be committees to go to service clubs and schools, to civil organizations (such as the fire and police department), and to sports organizations and kids groups. Wherever there is a possible chance to develop a lead, there need to be people in place to follow those leads and report back to the entire group what needs to be done.

KINDS OF FUNDRAISING

In chapter 10 we will discuss all kinds of events and ways to raise money. For now the group just needs to come up with ideas on how to find money. Write them down and make a list. Discuss what things make sense, and get rid of those that don't. Let the sky be your limit here. You never know what will work and what won't.

BASICS: ASK FOR AND TRY TO GET EVERYTHING DONATED!

Lists

I set this up as a special topic because lists can open doors that you never knew were there. Mailing lists of groups, organizations, churches, unions, schools, employees, patients, students—the list could go on forever—can help multiply your group's efforts by hundreds. Have someone in charge of compiling lists that can be utilized.

Meetings Scheduled

Do a basic outline on when and where meetings will be held. This allows volunteers and committee heads to invite people to join you. The media should always be invited to every meeting. Presidents of clubs and organizations should be encouraged to attend. Your own volunteers need to know when they will be expected to give reports on what is happening on the projects they are working on.

This example will give you a basic outline of what I have just written about. Follow it at your first meeting and you will have a starting point at which to begin. Discuss these things with your group, and they will have a better understanding of how everything can fit together. If you don't understand a section, refer back to that topic.

VOLUNTEER OUTLINE:
Getting Started

1. **Goals & Needs**
    A. Determine basic amounts for each person.
    B. Keep family at a distance.

2. **Time Frames**
    A. What are immediate needs?
    B. What kind of time do we have?
    C. Look realistically to each event and ask:
        "How much will be raised?"
        "In what time frame?"

3. **Accountability & Credibility**
    1. 501c3 usage
    2. Trustee to administer and approve funds
    3. How funds will be divided
    4. Bank accounts and any remaining money
    5. Who will actually pay the bills?
    6. Are two signatures required?
    7. Mailing address and contact phone number (donated voice mail)

4. **Commitment from Those Attending**
    Always ask everyone if, after they have heard everything that needs to be done, they are willing to continue to help. You need to know, and they need to give the commitment.

THE MEDIA

Like it or not, the media can make or break a fund-raising campaign. Raising money for an individual is much harder than raising money for an organization everyone has heard of, like the Boy Scouts. A newspaper or television station featuring your story can mean success. You will see faster results, and your efforts will make more money. Think of the media as an advertising agent for your fund-raising efforts, selling your story to many people faster and more effectively than you can yourself. The more people you can get involved, the more successful you will be.

It would be wise to have a committee chairperson to deal with the media. Ideally, this person would be connected to media in one way or another and needs to be outgoing, willing and able to draw an incredible picture of what you are trying to accomplish. A creative person who can come up with different ways to draw in the media can make your fund-raising much easier.

NEWSPAPERS

The written word travels far. You reach people in the comfort of their homes. Make sure they find your story worth reading.

Public service announcements, events, and meeting notices are not hard to get into the paper. All you do is write up what you want said and give it to the paper. Be sure to do this in plenty of time before the meeting or event. Ten days is not too early to submit your notice. Mail it, fax it, or hand deliver it; just be sure to get it there early. Examples are provided at the end of this chapter.

Direct your notice to the right editor. If you don't know who that is, ask the front desk person when you deliver the notice. Notices should be brought in on a continuing basis until your campaign is over. Regardless of what is being written in the paper about your story, you need to keep posting meeting times and the calendar of events being scheduled. It is even a good idea to follow the event with a story about how successful you were and where the campaign stands.

Some do's:

- Type your information in a neat and orderly fashion prefer-ably double spaced.
- Make sure you have the time, date, and location.
- State the nature and purpose of the meeting or event.
- State if (and how much) admission is being charged.
- State who is sponsoring the event
- Provide a brief description of what is going to happen
- Include a contact name and phone number for any ques-tions or inquiries.
- Consider using a picture. A black and white is best.

And don'ts:

- Don't phone in your notice.
- Don't ask the newspaper to run your item more than once.
- Don't ask the newspaper to promise the story will run on any specific day.

How do you get a story into the newspaper? Heartwarming sto-ries are easy to find. Newspapers like to publish stories of success and triumph especially around Christmas and Easter. They make good copy. Why are they reluctant to publish a story about little Susie needing money to save her life at other times of the year? Because there is always an overwhelming need for money, food, transplants, shelter, and whatever else comes up. Someone had a fire, or someone needs a bone marrow transplant, or someone's house was destroyed by a flood.

How does the newspaper justify helping one person and not everyone? Judgments are sometimes based on very cold and realistic choices. Which stories are the most interesting, compelling, or even easiest to write? How much space is available? Does the reporter have a personal interest in this particular story? All these factors affect whether your story appears on the front page, or anywhere in the paper at all.

Editors and reporters don't like to make the decision of who gets help (via a story) and who doesn't. John Bryd, ombudsman for the *Washington Post,* noted in a column that when what's needed is money for a lifesaving operation, "Editors are deciding who will live and who, lacking the funds that publicity will bring, will die." Some papers will not publish any story for this very reason. Some will publish stories if the person needing help lives in the circulation district of the paper.

After all is said and done, there is no clear-cut answer. Some papers will print stories and some won't. The following suggestions are only going to work part of time. However, there are ways to structure your story so it will at least be considered and have a better chance of making news. The bottom line: Newspapers do carry a lot of weight. With their help, you will be more effective. It is worth the effort to try to make the front page!

Suggestions

Find out what makes the patient special. The story of the young child and the forty-year-old truck driver referred to in chapter 1 is a real-life story. We turned the truck driver's story into one that every-one could relate to—a man losing his job and facing financial ruin because of an illness over which he had no control. Present this to the reporter, and make him or her feel what the father of that family was feeling. State your case and sell the idea.

Some of the other ideas that have worked in the past are:

- Another person hits the complicated journey through this country's health-care crisis.
- Granddaughter of well-known doctor faces medical treatment for which even Grandfather can't pay.
- Respected teacher faces medical crisis. Former students step up to help.
- 4-H girl faces transplant. Fellow members reach out and raise funds.
- Family of six facing medical obstacles when two children are diagnosed with potentially fatal disease.
- Small town rallies around farmer and raises money to test potential bone marrow donors.
- Star football player needs help. High school is building a mountain of money out of tin cans filled with money.
- Hospital refuses care to baby.

These are just a few of the ideas that have come forth and been effective in drawing in the media. These have worked for all forms of the media. To be successful:

1. Have an idea in mind before you approach any media source.
2. Know what you are asking for.
3. Be prepared for the interview.

TELEVISION

If you are not aware of the importance of instant everything, then you have been hiding in a cave. Today television is the number one source of news shaping the city, state, country, and world around you. How can you use this tool to help you reach your goals? As with newspapers, you need to establish your "hook."

When you are forming your committees, brainstorm ways of approaching the media. Come up with different ideas, and discuss which ones would work. What makes your story different from everyone else's? How can you get the reporter or even the entire station to jump on your bandwagon? It's not easy, but it can be done.

One family went to a television station and asked to speak to the reporter who every noon gives a presentation on medical problems. They complimented him on his show and explained that they were just everyday people who watched his program while they ate their lunch. The week prior their grandson had been diagnosed with cancer—something that isn't supposed to happen to a nine-year-old, freckled little guy. In one instant the entire family has been changed. Is there anything he can do to help?

Help? Yes, he might be able to help, and help he did. The reporter went to the station manager and asked to follow this family through their day-to-day struggle. He brought in experts to explain how people across the nation were coping with such difficult journeys. He gave daily updates on how much money had been raised and what events were coming up. He interviewed the family and showed pictures of the little guy going into the doctor's office and what it was like to face chemotherapy every three days for six months. Finally, when the family had reached its financial goals, he had a celebration party on the show. The boy thanked all the volunteers, who were also on the show, and the community for saving his life. The grandparents were there, but there was no mention of how their simple plea for help turned a potentially hopeless problem into a success story, one which an entire town followed from beginning to end.

RADIO

Normally, radio plays a public service role, and most stations devote a certain amount of time to public service announcements. It is beneficial to them, because they are promoting community goodwill. Using the same rules as listed for submitting newspaper notices, compose and submit service announcements to local radio stations; they will put them on the air as often as possible.

INTERVIEWS

Handling reporters can be a lot of fun, or a lot of trouble. A lot depends on the reporter, but even more depends on you. As in any endeavor, there are little tips—the best one being: *keep it simple*. One of the media people I worked with told me to craft my most important point so I could say it in less than fifteen seconds. For me, this is practically impossible. I can't say anything in just fifteen seconds! Notice: I'm writing a whole book! Be able to tell the reporter what you want him or her to tell the public. Choose one or two things and stress them strongly.

Always return reporters' calls. They are very busy, just as you are, but you must make sure they are behind your cause. No one likes to be ignored. Remember, you need them.

Before agreeing to be interviewed, ask the reporter what kind of questions to expect. You want to have all the information they will need, especially if you have a group of volunteers raising money for you and you haven't been in on all the events.

Regard the interview as an opportunity to tell your story the way you want it told. Realize, however, that the spoken word (your interview) and what appears in print may differ. Consider writing down what you want said, or at least key points, and don't be afraid to use your notes. You can even invite your campaign coordinator to come to the interview with you.

Go into the interview with a clear idea of what you want said. Have any calendars, written materials, or contact phone numbers handy when you go. Be prepared. Close with the key points you wanted stressed.

The people interviewing you are always contacts for future use. Get their business cards, and keep in touch with them. They can be a very important resource. If you didn't get into the door of one media outlet, don't give up. Be persistent; try someone else.

MEDIA RELEASE EXAMPLES

****

CENTRAL OREGON'S LARGEST SALE!!!!!
PARKING LOT / GARAGE SALE
~ PROCEEDS BENEFIT LITTLE SUSIE ~
Saturday June 6th, 8 A.M. to 4 P.M. at Grocery Stores A, B, and C
HOT DOG SALES…RADIO REMOTE CHALLENGES…
PRIZES…HOT AIR BALLOON RIDES…SPECIAL DISCOUNTS
AT LOCAL MERCHANTS…PIE AND ICE CREAM SALES…
RAFFLE PRIZES…IN-STORE DEMOS…SUPER BUYS WITH
LOTS TO CHOOSE FROM!
DONATIONS AND VOLUNTEERS NEEDED
PLEASE CALL: 111-1111
Deliver your tax deductible donations
Friday June 5th, noon to 5 P.M.
to either of the three grocery stores.
NO EARLY SALES!

****

* *

May 20, 1995
FOR IMMEDIATE RELEASE:
LITTLE SUSIE BENEFIT:
June 5th and 6th, 11:00 A.M. to 3:00 P.M.
Grocery Store A, B, and C
Contact: Susie Volunteer at 111-1111 or Joe Volunteer at 222-2222
Little Susie Benefit is an event benefiting Little Susie who is in need of a heart lung transplant. Central Oregon grocery stores A, B, and C are joining forces to help raise money for Little Susie's medically related expenses. Billed as Central Oregon's "Largest Garage Sale Ever," this event will be held in three locations all at the same time. Radio stations will be helping to raise money for Susie, as will Anyone's Pizza.

Donations and volunteers are needed. Please call today and come join the fun!

* *

LITTLE SUSIE BENEFIT GARAGE SALE
JUNE 6, 1992, 8 A.M.–4 P.M.
Three locations: Grocery Stores A, B and C
Donations can be made at Grocery Store A on June 5th, noon to 6 P.M.
WWWW radio remote…Joe Country
While you are there:
- Enjoy the hot dog and Pepsi sale: 2 hot dogs for $1 and get your Pepsi free.
- Spin the Wheel of Fortune and win a prize. Each chance will cost $.50.
- Donation jars will be inside the store.

* *

****

ANYONE'S PIZZA AND SUPERBIG HERO
WANT TO HELP LITTLE SUZIE

During the month of November:
- Say "Little Susie Benefit" at any *Anyone Pizza's* Central Oregon location and receive $1 off your pizza. *Anyone's* will match that $1 and give it to Little Susie.
- Say "Little Susie" at Superbig Hero and $1 of every $5 purchase and half of all brownie sales will be donated to Little Susie.

****

Somewhere Grocery Store Hosts Little Suzie Benefit
Parking lot sale from 8 A.M. to 4 P.M. on Saturday June 6th.
Donations can be made inside the store June 5th, noon to 6 P.M.
Joe Country, of XXXX 111 Country Radio, will be broadcasting live.
Donation jars will be inside the store.
Apple Pie and Ice Cream Sale
    All proceeds go to Little Susie. The pie and ice cream were donated by XYX Dairy and Somewhere Grocery Store.
Life-Core Raffle
    The *Outdoor Package of Prizes* (which includes a voucher for a weekend at SunTown by the coast) is on display at the store until July 4th, when the raffle drawing will be held at the Museum of the Sage. Ticket sales ($1 each or 12 for $10) will start June 10th. This *Outdoor Package of Prizes* was donated by local merchants.
Hot-air balloon rides: Make a donation and take a ride.
Banana split super sale.
Hot Dog and Pepsi sale: 2 hot dogs for $1 and get your Pepsi free.
In-store product demos: Come sample the best!

****

****

NOTES FOR ZZZZ TV INTERVIEW:

Volunteers:	36 volunteers at each location to help with parking lot sales, hot dog sales, setup, and takedown duties.
Donations:	Bring donations to any participating store Friday, noon to 5 P.M.
	Call Susie Volunteer 111-1111 for free pickup.
Special Attractions:	Live radio remotes, hot-air balloon rides, hot dog sales
	Apple pie and ice cream social,
	$1 off pizzas
	$1 off Superbig Hero Sandwiches
Benefiting:	Little Susie, who needs a heart-lung transplant

****

TEN

WHAT WORKS AND WHAT DOESN'T

If you have a bake sale and sell 50 cakes at $10 each, 150 cupcakes at $1 each, and 25 pies at $10 each, how much money will you raise? If you have a garage sale and have people donate all their sellable items and you make $500 in one day, how much money will you raise? If you wash 1,000 cars at $3 a piece and add that to your total, how much will you have now? How close are you to raising $300,000?

The above three ways of making money are done all the time by everyone from the housewife down the street to national organizations. They are great ways to earn money, but how many bake sales, car washes, and garage sales does it take to raise $300,000—or even $30,000?

Most fund-raising ideas make money; the trick is to make sure they can raise enough to justify your valuable time and energy. In this chapter the idea is to give you an idea of how to *develop* and *expand* ideas so they can *maximize* your resources.

At your very first organizational meeting, after you have done all the things we have discussed in the previous chapters, you must implement a plan of action. Discuss volunteers' ideas on how to raise money. Each and every idea is a viable way to put money in the bank. When you *develop* the idea of having a garage sale, you need to *expand* it to make it double or even triple what an ordinary sale would do. Usually, the purpose of a garage sale is to clean out the garage and maybe make some money. Our purpose is to save someone's life. We need lots of money to do that, so you need to maximize the resources you have and make this garage sale bigger, better, and more successful than any other garage sale that has ever been held.

Let's pretend you have fifty volunteers to help with your garage sale. Why not have fifty garage sales all on the same day at different locations with items donated to all fifty volunteers? You can advertise it on television so each and every sale is linked to the next one. A PROGRESSIVE GARAGE SALE! At the end of this chapter are some fliers, news releases, and actual check-off lists I used for sales held at four different shopping malls throughout Central Oregon all on the same day. Was the event successful? About $7,000 worth! Better than the $500 an ordinary sale would have raised. If you are going to be doing it anyway, DO IT BIG!

Most everything can be successful, but to what degree? You need to be more than successful. If your group is having a hard time coming up with ideas for events, go to the library for books on fund-raising. Adapt them to your needs. Most fund-raising books are for raising money for groups. You are unique because you are doing it for one person. The ideas you will find will work for a group or an individual; you just need to adapt.

PIGGYBACKING

This is an idea I have used many times, and it seems to work for all kinds of different events. When you are having your organizational meeting, have a calendar from your Chamber of Commerce, newspaper, or whatever list of upcoming events in your area. Find out what is already being scheduled, and ask the sponsors if you can be a part of their event.

THE COUNTY FAIR

One of my patients was a member of 4-H. She needed a transplant, so we organized street dances the nights of the fair. Fair sponsors included in their advertising that they supported the Susie Smith Fund-raising Drive and asked for donations and help. One of the 4-H kids offered her cow. It was auctioned off at the fair, and the proceeds went to Susie. At the concert one evening 4-H volunteers passed a special hat so people could make donations right there.

ANNUAL CHRISTMAS CRAFT FAIR

I know of a group that went to every craft fair throughout October, November, and December. Its members handed out fliers asking vendors to have an "After Christmas Blowout Sale." The volunteers got the building (at no cost), advertised it (at no cost), and set it up. The vendors not only paid to be there by renting tables, but they also gave a percentage of their earnings. The volunteers sold baked good (the ever-present bake sale) and drinks. Money was made off other people's efforts.

SUPER BOWL SUNDAY

Now how could you be involved in the Super Bowl? A high school Boys Athletic Group decided they wanted to help a teacher who was the object of a citywide fund-raising drive. They got together with all the pizza parlor owners in the town and arranged to handle all the deliveries for Super Bowl Sunday if the owners would donate a percentage of each pizza sold that day. The boys advertised it in the newspaper and TV (all donated time and space), and each pizza parlor name was listed. Every pizza parlor owner agreed to do it! (Would you like to be the only one that didn't?) The guys not only raised money from the pizza sale, but because it was so well advertised, and the cause had already been made known to the community, they made great tips!

In every town there are always things going on. Service clubs, such as Eagles, Elks, and Lions, usually have events scheduled. Even if you do nothing more than offer to have your volunteers park cars at an event for $1 a car, you can piggyback off of someone's endeavors. The trick is to help others accomplish what they need to get done. The Christmas sale is a great example! Vendors want to get rid of the things they did not sell during the holiday season. You help them, and they help you. As they say, a win-win situation!

POTLUCK DINNER

I have always wanted to try this one, and to my knowledge no one has before. Especially in small towns, when there needs to be a meeting of some kind, it seems like the women always get together and have a potluck dinner. When I was president of a local Lions group, I always had the women plan potlucks because they were such great cooks! Now picture this! You go to the local baseball park and find out how to get the park donated. Line up some entertainment—bands, a craft sale, a kids fun and games day—something to bring people in. Then contact every women's group in town and ask that they have each member bring a dish to the event. Have the local soda pop company donate drinks. Advertise it well in the newspaper and on TV; paste fliers all over town. State that anyone bringing a pot of something receives dinner for the family at a reduced rate. Charge everyone say $3 to $5 to eat at the "FIRST ANNUAL BIGGEST POTLUCK DINNER EVER." This would be an excellent "piggyback" for little league playoffs, or maybe a statewide softball tournament. It could work on the fourth of July if held where people could sit and watch the fireworks! The possibilities are unlimited!

CANISTER CAMPAIGN

Everyone of us has seen a canister of some kind in a store or restaurant with a plea for donations to help someone. A great deal of money can be raised this way, but there are some guidelines you need to follow. If you do, you can have this project going on while other events are taking place.

- Have one or two people in charge of this project, but have a large number of volunteers willing to help distribute and collect the canisters.

- Make a list of where canisters are being placed. This is the most important task.

- Divide your town into specific areas so one person can be in charge of a certain number of canisters in a certain area. When looking for locations to place the canisters, make sure the business has lots of traffic. Try to put the canister as close to the cash register as possible.

- Keep an updated list of all canister locations, the person in charge at the business and which volunteer is responsible for the canister. On your list put the date when the canister was placed and later picked up.

- The canister should clearly state all important information (whom you are helping and why). Make sure all canisters have a sticker or writing on the bottom listing whom to call if help is needed.

- Make a schedule of when the money is to be picked up. This needs to be done daily when there is an active campaign going on. This should be done by the same person each time, and the money should be taken directly to the bank where it can be counted by a teller. The teller should give the collector a receipt for the deposit.

- Be sure you can trust the person doing the collecting, or have two people go together. There is no way of knowing how much is being collected until it is counted.

- Have a specific time frame for canisters being out. When the time is up, collect *all* the canisters at once. Going into a business, asking for their help, geting it, and then forgetting about them creates ill will and hinders the next person's efforts to use this method for fund-raising.

- A letter should be given to the person going to a business and collecting the funds. This way the business knows the collector is a legitimate volunteer. Here is a sample:

TO WHOM IT MAY CONCERN:

The bearer of this letter, _____
(name of the collector), is authorized by the volunteer group helping _____ (patient's name) to collect the contents of the containers placed in your store. If you have any questions or concerns please feel free to call _____
(committee chairperson) at _____
(phone number). Thank you for your support.

The most important issue in this chapter is to realize that you can make money by doing everything that has already been done. Just do it bigger and better. Put a new twist on it. You can make money by doing new things. The sky's the limit when it comes to creating new and innovative ways of making money. Step out of your comfort zone, and use your imagination.

The key is to figure out realistically how much can be raised. As I said earlier, it takes a lot of cars at $3 each to raise $300,000.

Always keep other projects in some stage of completion. This is another reason why it is so important to have as many volunteers helping as you can. Each volunteer brings a different group of people and ideas to the table.

IDEAS

I am including this list so you will have somewhere to start. Take an idea and expand on it. Ask yourself how your town is different from others and what will work for your particular area.

1. Selling services. Kids are great at this. Don't just think of car washes. How about:
   - dog-sitting or walking
   - watering yards or yard cleanup
   - a gift-wrapping service during the holidays
2. General auctions (more on that later)
3. Auto auction: Get a dealership to donate a car, boat, truck, or whatever.
4. Arts and crafts shows
5. Dances
6. Grand Galas
7. Concerts (indoor or outdoor)
8. Any kind of food event (pancake breakfasts, etc.)
9. Any kind of *A-Thon:* bike, walk, swim, sing, any kind
10. Casino nights
11. Art sales
12. Pizza nights
13. Fairs
14. Theater benefits
15. Any kind of *social:* ice cream, spaghetti, chili
16. Sports competitions
17. Special film showings. Have a premiere night for a new show in town and have a special showing.
18. Bowling for $$$
19. Door-to-door. This might be against the law, so check with the city first.
20. Radio Station Promos. Disc jockeys challenge each other: Who can raise the most money?

As you can see, the list could go on and on. The following are some hints, samples, and information on some fund-raisers I have worked on. Use what you want and make up what you need.

****

CENTRAL OREGON CLEAN-UP AND CLEAN-OUT PARKING LOT SALES

WHEN: June 5th, noon to 5 P.M.; June 6th, 8 A.M. to 4 P.M.

WHERE: All Central Oregon grocery stores

WHY: To benefit Life-Core, the Central Oregon Bone Marrow Transplant Foundation. This benefit is to raise money for Life-Core so it can continue to help patients and families facing transplants.

HOW CAN YOU HELP?

Donate items. Call Life-Core (phone #) or (alternate name and phone number).

Donate time the day of the sale.

Volunteer to organize the sale.

Give a cash donation.

Sell hot dogs.

Help set up and take down.

Write thank-you responses.

Prepare local media updates.

****

Attention XYZ Store Employees:

CENTRAL OREGON CLEAN-UP AND CLEAN-OUT PARKING LOT SALE

LIFE-CORE NEEDS YOUR LEFTOVERS!

WHY: Life-Core is teaming up with Central Oregon stores to raise money so Life-Core can help patients and families facing bone marrow transplants.

WHEN: Sale: June 6th (8 A.M. to 4 P.M.) No early sales.

Donations: June 5th, noon to 6 P.M.

WHERE: At every grocery store parking lot in Bend, Redmond, and Prineville.

QUESTIONS: Please contact Life-Core at (phone number).

BONUSES:

All donations tax deductible	Radio remote challenges
Hot dog sales	Prizes and raffles
Hot-air balloon rides	Special discounts at local merchants
Pie and ice cream sales	In-store demos

Super buys with lots to choose from!

All Benefiting Life-Core:
The Central Oregon Bone Marrow Transplant Foundation

****

LOCAL COORDINATORS CHECK-OFF LIST

DONATED STORAGE UNIT:

Name:

Contact Person:

Address: Phone:

Name:

Contact Person:

Address   Phone:

Tables Donated By:

Contact Person:

Pickup address:

When: Phone:

OVERNIGHT SECURITY:

Prineville   Phone

Redmond   Phone

North Bend   Phone

South Bend   Phone

END OF SALE PICKUP:

Organization Name: Phone:

Contact Person: Will have truck? Y____ N____

If no pickup, where we will deliver to:

Contact Person: Phone

Volunteer time schedules turned into Diane: Y____ N____

Coordinator Name:

****

Dear Volunteers:

I want to thank all of you for offering to help at the Central Oregon Clean-up and Clean-out Parking Lot Sales. Pulling off four sales in two days in three towns should be quite a challenge. Many of you have expressed concern about not having done this before. I will try to guide you through this entire project. If you have any questions or concerns, please just give me a call. Janet and Suzan are veteran "salers" and they, too, can answer most of your questions.

We will be kicking off the donation drive the first week in May. This will give us an entire month to collect items. The Life-Core board members will be actively seeking donations from various places. I have already asked the grocery store employees to help. Please don't wait for us to come up with ideas on where to get donations; use your imagination.

I will be completing the news releases and fliers within the next week and hope to have everything ready to go by the next Life-Core board meeting (April 16th, 5:30 P.M. at the Life-Core office). Everyone is invited to attend. If you aren't there, I will make sure you receive everything you need. If I miss something, please just let us know.

Please read the enclosed information. If you have questions, yell. Go introduce yourself to the manager of the grocery store you will be working with. Line up those storage units. Most of all, please have fun doing this. It is for a great cause!

Thanks again for all your help!

****

RAFFLE INFORMATION

Raffles are illegal in some states. Call your Attorney General's office to make sure you know what your state allows.

Raffle logbook must list:

Total amount of proceeds
All expenses
The winning ticket stubs
Names of all volunteers and employees selling tickets
Number of tickets received by each seller
Number of purchased tickets by each seller
Amount of money from ticket sales by each seller

Requirements for prizes awarded over $100 value:

Name of organization
Date of drawing
Description of prize
Name and address of winner
Signature of winner
Receipt from seller/distributor for noncash prizes with retail value of over $500

Prior to sales

Submit a raffle notice containing:

Name of organization

Organization raffle license number

Location, date, and time of draw

Description and retail value of prize

Number of tickets to be offered for sale and the price of
each ticket

Copy of the sample ticket

Each ticket must state:

(This may be done on a flier as long as it is given out at the time
the ticket is purchased.)

"Winner need not be present to win."

Date and time of drawing

Location of drawing

Organization's name

Price of the ticket

Retail market value of each prize

Total number of tickets which my be sold

Full and fair description of the prizes or prize to be awarded

Operation of the raffle:

All tickets must have an equal chance at winning.

No person may be required to buy more than one ticket.

No person must be required to be present to win.

Each seller must return all ticket stubs to organization.

All ticket stubs must be put into a receptacle out of which the
winning tickets will be drawn.

No unsold tickets shall be entered in the draw container or otherwise be considered for the drawing.

Unclaimed prizes shall be held in trust for a period of one year
from the date of the draw. If at that time the prizes are still
unclaimed, they will be donated to the organization.

No tickets may be sold prior to twelve months before the drawing.

If for any reason the raffle is not completed and prizes are not awarded on the scheduled drawing date, organization must take all steps necessary to notify ticket purchasers of the fact and return all money received from the ticket purchasers within thirty days.

Raffle reports and records:

Must be kept for three years

Must list total amount of proceeds received from each raffle

Must list all expenses relating to the conduct of each raffle

Must contain the winning ticket stub

Must include the raffle logbook with all related information contained therein

Annual Report (due within sixty days after the end of the raffle year and must include):

Number of raffle games held during the year

Date of each drawing

Total sales of each game

Total expenses relating to the conduct of the game

Total amount of cash prizes and the total cost to the licensee of all noncash items

Total expenses of all games expressed as a percentage of the total raffle handled

The net income from raffle games

The signature of a responsible official of the organization

Copy of Annual Fee made payable to the Department of Justice

Amount shall be one-half of 1percent of the handle listed in the report.

Expect a delinquency fee of $20 or 1 percent of the fee (whichever is greater) if not delivered to the Department of Justice by due date.

****

RAFFLE NOTICE

DATE:

LOCATION OF RAFFLE:

DATE OF DRAWING:

TIME OF DRAWING:

PERSON OR REASON FOR DRAWING:

CONTACT PERSON:

ADDRESS:

HOME PHONE: WORK PHONE:

NUMBER OF TICKETS TO BE SOLD:

PURCHASE PRICE OF TICKETS:

COPY OF SAMPLE TICKET   YES   NO

DESCRIPTION OF PRIZES   RETAIL VALUE

1. _____   _____

2. _____   _____

3. _____   _____

4. _____   _____

5. _____   _____

6. _____   _____

****

RAFFLE DRAWING FOLLOW-UP REPORT

LOCATION OF DRAWING:

DATE OF DRAWING:

TIME OF DRAWING:

PERSON OR REASON FOR DRAWING:

CONTACT PERSON:

NUMBER OF TICKETS SOLD: PRICE   OF

TICKET:

TOTAL AMOUNT OF PROCEEDS:

TOTAL AMOUNT OF EXPENSES:

LIST OF ALL EXPENSES:

THE WINNING TICKET STUB ENCLOSED: YES__ NO__

COPY OF RAFFLE LOG SHEET ENCLOSED: YES__ NO__

NAME OF WINNER:

ADDRESS OF WINNER:

PHONE NUMBER:

WINNER'S STATEMENT ENCLOSED: YES__ NO__

****

RAFFLE LOG INFORMATION:

DATE OF DRAWING: TIME:

PERSON OR REASON FOR DRAWING:

CONTACT PERSON:

TICKET SELLERS:

    NAME:

    ADDRESS:

    PHONE NUMBER:

    NAME:

    ADDRESS:

    PHONE NUMBER:

    NAME:

    ADDRESS:

    PHONE NUMBER:

NUMBER OF TICKETS RECEIVED: DATE:

SIGNATURE:

NUMBER OF TICKETS SOLD: TOTAL AMOUNT:

TOTAL AMOUNT TURNED IN: DATE:

SIGNATURE:

****

WINNING PRIZE TICKET

RAFFLE PURPOSE:

DESCRIPTION OF PRIZE:

NAME OF WINNER:

ADDRESS OF WINNER:

CITY: STATE: ZIP:

DAYTIME PHONE NUMBER: EVENING PHONE:

DATE NOTIFIED:

DATE PRIZE PICKED UP:

SIGNATURE OF WINNER:

****

AUCTIONS

DATE & TIME OF AUCTION:

PERSON OR REASON FOR AUCTION:

PLACE OF AUCTION:

CONTACT PERSON:

   ADDRESS:

   HOME PHONE: WORK PHONE:

DESCRIPTION OF PRIZES   RETAIL VALUE / SOLD FOR

1._____   _____

2._____   _____

3._____   _____

4._____   _____

****

AUCTION FORMAT

Set your goals.

Safety factor: Your goal should be 75 percent of retail value.

Multiply goal by 1,333 percent.

Example: Goal $15,000

                         x 1.333

                         $19,995

$20,000 retail value needs to be donated.

$20,000 retail value x 75 percent = $15,000 desired goal.

Get volunteers.

Look for people who are visible, positive, responsible, and fun.

Positions to fill:

Chairperson

Needs to be aggressive and highly organized.

Honorary Chairperson

Must be visible, able to bring credibility to event, and will

ing to be a figurehead.

Cochairperson

Follows through and picks up loose ends.

Merchandise Chairperson

Picks up items.

Arranges storage for items prior to auction.

Arranges delivery to auction and display.

<u>Publicity Chairperson</u>

Promotes the solicitation of donated items.

Promotes the event.

Handles news conferences with Honorary Chairperson.

<u>Location and Decoration Chairperson</u>

Finds the location for the event.

Decorates for the event.

Arranges catering (if required).

A no host bar helps the sales, but remember why you are having the event. If the person has lung cancer or cancer of the liver, liquor might not be a great thing to have.

Arranges any entertainment if wanted.

This is usually during the first part of the event while people are taking part in the silent auction time. Once the auction starts there really isn't any need for entertainment; the auction itself provides excitement.

<u>Operation Chairperson</u>

Arranges for (or hires) auctioneer, clerk, cashier, and people to handle registration, hold up items, and provide security. A service organization (such as a Lions, Rotary, or Kiwanis Club) might volunteer.

<u>Cleanup Chairperson</u>

Makes sure everything is picked up and ready to get back to normal. If this event is held at a hotel, the hotel staff might cleanup, but there are always items to move or take back home.

<u>Follow-Up Chairperson</u>

Follows up on the mailing list to mail out thank-you cards.

Requests feedback on how the event could have been better.

Obtain Donated Items

General:

Write a letter to businesses and groups.

Contact churches.

Organize media appeals for help.

Special:

Target certain items that fit the objective.

For example, if patient is a car mechanic, go to other mechanics and ask for services and products (even a donated car).

Have target items meet 50 percent of your retail goal.

Focus on special people who might lend a hand with other donations.

If possible, have your Honorary Chairman get special donations, but don't make an issue of it. You don't want to lose that person.

General Information

Selecting the location:

Keep in mind the size of the room and how many might attend.

Is there a sound system?

Round tables are best.

Decide what food should be served and if it can be donated.

Four groups of items to be auctioned:

1. Door Prizes (like a donated trip to bring in people)
2. Raffle prizes (items of small value); sell tickets at the door (about $1 each)
3. Silent auction (items not really big enough to bring in the big bucks)
4. Oral auction (the biggest and best donated items)

Get the auction started with a bang.

Music—upbeat

Motivational or inspirational speaker

Talk about why they are there, where their money will go.

Explain that if more is raised than what is needed, it will go to help other patients.

Get everything donated.

Room, food, auctioneer, storage, printing, everything.

Number each item as it comes in.

This number will stay with the item until it has been sold and paid for.

Have a donation jar at the door. Ask for a $5 donation (like a cover charge).

Find a business with high visibility.

Ask if items can be dropped off at that business location.

See if you can use its phone number as a contact for people wanting to donate. If so, provide donation sheets so employees can write down the information and pass it on to you.

Explain that this publicity will include free advertising in the event for helping. (Besides, the community sevice they are providing is good for their image).

Try to find someone that will let you use their MasterCard or Visa credit card system.

****

AUCTION DONATIONS

Volunteer's Name:

Address:

Daytime Phone: Evening Phone:

Confirmed Items:

Item: Retail value:

Donor name: Phone:

If donor will deliver, the date and time:

If arrangements for pickup must be made, list date, time, person who will do this:

    Item: Retail value:

    Donor name: Phone:

    If donor will deliver, the date and time:

If arrangements for pickup must be made, list date, time, person who will do this:

Pending Items:

    Item: Retail value:

    Donor name: Phone:

    Item: Retail value:

    Donor name: Phone:

Prospects:

    Item: Retail value:

    Donor name: Phone:

    Item: Retail value:

    Donor name: Phone:

Please mail or hand deliver this sheet by (date) to:

(Name of Merchandise Chairperson), Merchandise Chairperson

    Address:

    Phone:

****

ELEVEN

CONCLUDING YOUR

FUND-RAISING CAMPAIGN

Thank You! Thank You! Thank You! Thank You! Thank You! Thank You! Thank You! Thank You! Thank You! Thank You! Thank You! Thank You! Thank You! Thank You! Thank You! Thank You! Thank You! You! Thank You! Thank You! Thank You! Thank You! Thank You! Thank You! Thank You! Thank You! Thank You! Thank You! Thank You! You! Thank You! Thank You! Thank You! Thank You! Thank You! Thank You! Thank You! Thank You! Thank You! Thank You! Thank You! You! Thank You! Thank You! Thank You!

Get the picture? Thanking everyone is so important. Your list is as long as the dollars that were raised. Everyone needs to be thanked —volunteers, businesses, donors, doctors, everyone. There are many ways to do this, so I'll just touch on a few. The most important thing is to do it.

One family went to the local television station about doing a news story/follow-up to the stories they had been running about the fund-raising campaign. The news team went to the family's home, and, while being interviewed, all the family members publicly said their *thank-yous.*

Another family owned a pizza parlor. They had a free pizza day for the community. An unexpected bonus: The distributors that delivered to the pizza parlor heard what the family was doing and why and arranged for the food to be donated!

One patient spent her hospital stay writing thank-you notes for every dollar she could trace. She made a game of opening the mail each day that was sent directly to her, making a list of contributors she got cards from, and sending out her own thank-you letters. Many times she wasn't well enough to go to an event, but she always sent a letter or card to be read at the event. After the money was collected, she asked the volunteers to copy the checks that were written, so she could get the addresses off them. She was often too sick to talk, but she always wrote her notes.

People ask me how I can do what I do after having my daughter die. Well, people like I have described validate how very blessed I am to be working with such patients and families.

It does not make any difference how you thank people. You can take an advertisement in the newspaper. The main point is to make some kind of effort to let people know you appreciate what they have given.

DOT YOUR I'S AND CROSS YOUR T'S

Before calling a halt to the fund-raising operations, have at least one completion meeting with all the volunteers. You need to (1) congratulate yourselves and (2) make sure everyone has finished his/her share of the campaign.

Some questions that need to be asked are: Are all store canisters accounted for? Have they all been picked up? Are all check out sheets completed and turned in? I once had a group put out canisters. More than six months after the campaign was completed a grocery store owner called and asked if our group was the one responsible for "these things sitting on my counter for the last year." As much as I hated admitting it, we had dropped the ball. I had to go pick up the canisters and explain their importance—which seemed out of kilter for our not having picked it up in the first place. It was not a fun trip, and I am now very careful about making sure all canisters are accounted for.

Have all funds been turned in? Many volunteers are involved in just one event. Sometimes they don't even know when the fund-raising campaign ends. Take your calendar of events, check off each event, and make sure all the volunteers and funds are accounted for.

If you worked through a church, nonprofit organization, or civic club, have you filled out any forms or reports and turned them in? Many civic clubs keep a total of what their organization raised (and for whom) during the year. This goes on an annual report given to members and boards of directors. Just a quick completion tally along with a thank-you note is all you need to do.

This list could go on and on. The most important thing to remember is to make sure that all protocols and "to do" items have been completed.

Finally, the media can once again help you complete your story. Invite the reporter to your final meeting. Give a completed, typed report of your group's results. Invite the reporter to follow through on the patient's progress. Provide story as well as medical updates. The reporter can also ask readers if anyone has additional funds to turn in, or any unfinished business they wish to take care of via a person's name and phone number.

TWELVE

WRAPPING UP—

WHATEVER YOU RAISED

IS ENOUGH!

When all this started, your group made goals. Sometimes these goals are not met. Sometimes they are far exceeded. Whatever you raised is more than what the patient had in the beginning. You need to make sure that every volunteer knows that it was all worth it. Some of the best goals are never written down. They are the ones that, when achieved, reflect the support and love that went into all that was done. To this day, I bring out the newspaper clippings and read about the support and love that went out to Michelle. I thank God that so many people cared enough to pray for our family. Without them and without God, we would not have made it.

MORE REALITIES

The experience of walking the walk with my daughter, and many others, has taught me many valuable lessons in dealing with relationships. The impact of major illnesses extends far beyond the patient. Families are drawn into a world that requires keeping things normal amidst chaos and keeping the family intact even when members are far away, physically and/or emotionally. The patient must deal with the medical side of surviving; the family members must try to keep the family, financial, and emotional structures intact. There are some very valuable things we can all do to make this journey easier.

- Gain all the information you can about the disease and treatment of your loved one. Information is the key to understanding what and why things are happening to those we love. Gilda Radner, in her book *It's Always Something,* explained what chemotherapy was like better than any doctor could. She said it was like putting your finger into a light socket and not being able to take it out. I never started reading about Shelly's disease or treatment until after she had gone to heaven. If I had, I really believe I would have been more understanding about what she was going through. I realize you barely have time to turn around, but there are times (i.e., waiting for doctors) when you can pull out a book or magazine and gain information.

- Get medical information directly from the doctor or nurses treating your loved one. Secondhand information passed on by the patient can become very different than what is really happening. Go to appointments with the patient as often as possible. Information really can reduce the stress levels you are feeling.

- Try to control what you are taking on as far as outside demands. If a spouse is ill, you are elected the caregiver to the patient, chief baby-sitter, housekeeper, financial advisor, and everything in between. Overload is a common burnout factor for those trying to accomplish everything. You need to be realistic about what you can handle. Seek additional help from others. After the fund-raising campaign is off the ground, step back and let others take the ball. Concentrate on what you need to do to complete your own tasks.

- Find a friend or friends you can turn to just for yourself. Talk about what is going on. Let them shoulder some of the sadness and most of all the triumphs you are experiencing with your loved one. There are wonderful support groups out there that can help you understand what is going on and how to survive it. Turn to them. The time you take out for yourself will give you a better attitude toward your sick loved one.

- Know there will be times when you feel like kicking everyone and everything around you. Accept that and know you can get through it. Make up your mind that you are going to stick together and grow stronger, no matter what. Realize that patients often take out the frustration of their illness on those closest to them. Try to not take it to heart; know that they really do love you and they are just up against walls they don't have the strength to climb by themselves. Laugh with them and cry with them. Understand that they like you, are doing everything they can to get over this disease.

THE TOUGHEST REALITY OF ALL

The final and toughest reality of life is the reality of death. Not one of us will live forever. Even ten years after saying good-bye to Shelly, I still remember her illness, every aspect of her struggle to live—the good and the bad. It was Shelly's will to live that gave her strength to fight, and fight she did. The reality is that God had other plans. All our prayers and efforts couldn't keep her with us. We never talked about her dying, because, according to her, she had to see her little boy grow up. We handled everything the best we could at the time. Looking back, I can say there were many wonderful days and many not so wonderful days.

Don't wait until the fight is coming to a close before you hold your loved one and tell them, over and over, that you love them. Now that Shelly is in heaven, I hope she can still hear me. Even though I said it all the time, I could never tell her enough how much I loved her. By helping others, I truly feel I am still helping Shell. When I see her again, I will be able to tell her: "I couldn't help you, but I did the best I could." Please know that is all that we can do.

There are three things that remain —
faith,
hope,
love—
and the greatest of these is love.

CORINTHIANS 13:13, TLB

The End

Check any of the following boxes if you would like to receive additional infromation about Diane Tolley or order quantity numbers of books for your organization or business. Please mail to:

Diane Tolley
P.O. Box 971
Bend, Oregon 97709

or e-mail your request to:
tolley@coinet.com

_____ I would like more books:*
One _____
Ten _____
Twenty _____
More _____
*Special pricing for quantity orders
_____ I would like Diane to consult with me individually.
_____ I would like Diane to speak before my group, organization, or business.
_____ I would like Diane to hold a training session for my group, organization, or business.

Do you have questions or comments?

_____

_____

_____

Name_____
Address_____
City_____ ST_____ Zip_____
Phone_____ E-mail_____